The Pilgrim's Progress—Frontispiece.

"'A BOOK IN HIS HAND AND A GREAT BURDEN UPON HIS BACK.'"

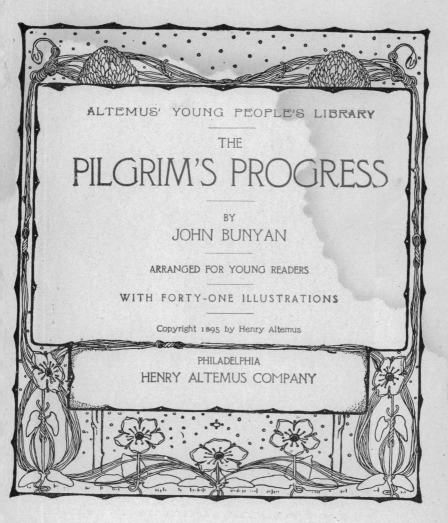

ALTEMUS' YOUNG PEOPLE'S LIBRARY

THE

PILGRIM'S PROGRESS

BY

JOHN BUNYAN

ARRANGED FOR YOUNG READERS

WITH FORTY-ONE ILLUSTRATIONS

PHILADELPHIA
HENRY ALTEMUS COMPANY

PREFACE.

THE PILGRIM'S PROGRESS is the most popular story-book in the world. With the exception of the Bible it has been translated into more languages than any other book ever printed.

John Bunyan is one of the two or three greatest writers of pure English. His style is a perfect model of simple, straight, plain and delightful writing.

A demand seems to exist for an edition of this established work more suited to young people with our latter day tastes. The story is here told in Bunyan's precise words. In a very few instances the text has been shortened but in no case mutilated; and his teachings and all the doctrinal features of his marvellous allegory are untouched.

The first edition of the book was issued in 1678, and more than 100,000 copies were sold in the twenty years following its appearance.

It is hoped that the present copiously illustrated edition may lead young readers to an appreciation of the author, and a further acquaintance with the facts in his eventful life.

He composed and published many other works, some of great practical usefulness; but these were eclipsed by the lasting fame and popularity attained by this his greatest production.

vi   AS I SLEPT I DREAMED A DREAM.

THE AUTHOR'S APOLOGY FOR HIS BOOK.

WHEN at the first I took my pen in hand.
    Thus for to write, I did not understand
That I at all should make a little book
In such a mode; nay, I had undertook
To make another; which, when almost done,
Before I was aware, I this begun.

    And thus it was: I, writing of the way
And race of saints in this our gospel-day,
Fell suddenly into an allegory
About their journey and the way to glory,
In more than twenty things, which I set down:
This done. I twenty more had in my crown;
And then again began to multiply,
Like sparks that from the coals of fire do fly.
Nay, then, thought I, if that you breed so fast,
I'll put you by yourselves, lest you at last
Should prove *ad infinitum*, and eat out
The book that I already am about.

    Well, so I did; but yet I did not think
To show to all the world my pen and ink
In such a mode; I only thought to make
I knew not what; nor did I undertake
Thereby to please my neighbor; no, not I;
I did it mine own self to gratify.

Neither did I but vacant seasons spend
In this my scribble; nor did I intend
But to divert myself, in doing this,
From worser thoughts, which make me do amiss.

Thus I set pen to paper with delight,
And quickly had my thoughts in black and white.
For having now my method by the end,
Still as I pull'd, it came; and so I penn'd
It down; until at last it came to be,
For length and breadth, the bigness which you see.

Well, when I had thus put my ends together,
I showed them others, that I might see whether
They would condemn them, or them justify;
And some said, Let them live; some, Let them die
Some said, John, print it; others said, Not so:
Some said, It might do good; others said, No.

Now was I in a strait, and did not see
Which was the best thing to be done by me:
At last I thought, Since you are thus divided,
I print it will: and so the case decided.

For, thought I, some I see would have it done,
Though others in that channel do not run:
To prove, then, who advised for the best,
Thus I thought fit to put it to the test.

I further thought, if now I did deny
Those that would have it thus to gratify,
I did not know, but hinder them I might
Of that which would to them be great delight:
For those which were not for its coming forth,
I said to them, Offend you I am loath:
Yet, since your brethren pleased with it be,
Forbear to judge, till you do further see.

If that thou wilt not read, let it alone;
Some love the meat, some love to pick the bone;
Yea, that I might them better moderate,
I did too with them thus expostulate:

May I not write in such a style as this?
In such a method, too, and yet not miss
My end, thy good?   Why may it not be done?
Dark clouds bring waters, when the bright bring none.
Yea, dark or bright, if they their silver drops
Cause to descend, the earth, by yielding crops,
Gives praise to both, and carpeth not at either,
But treasures up the fruit they yield together;
Yea, so commixes both, that in their fruit
None can distinguish this from that; they suit
Her well when hungry; but if she be full,
She spews out both, and makes their blessing null.

You see the ways the fisherman doth take
To catch the fish; what engines doth he make.
Behold! how he engageth all his wits;
Also his snares, lines, angles, hooks, and nets:
Yet fish there be that neither hook nor line,
Nor snare, nor net, nor engine, can make thine:
They must be groped for, and be tickled too,
Or they will not be catch'd, whate'er you do.
How does the fowler seek to catch his game?
By divers means, all which one cannot name:
His guns, his nets, his lime-twigs, light, and bell;
He creeps, he goes, he stands; yea, who can tell
Of all his postures?   Yet there's none of these
Will make him master of what fowls he please.
Yea, he must pipe and whistle to catch this,
Yet, if he does so, that bird he will miss.

If that a pearl may in a toad's head dwell,
And may be found, too, in an oyster shell:
If things that promise nothing do contain
What better is than gold, who will disdain.

That have an inkling of it there to look,
That they may find it ? Now, my little book
(Though void of all these paintings that may make
It with this or the other man to take)
Is not without those things that do excel
What do in brave but empty notions dwell.

Well, yet I am not fully satisfied,
That this your book will stand when soundly tried.

Why, what's the matter ? It is dark ! What though ?
But it is feigned. What of that, I trow ?
Some men, by feigned words, as dark as mine,
Make truth to spangle, and its rays to shine !
But they want solidness. Speak, man, thy mind !
They drown the weak ; metaphors make us blind.

Solidity, indeed, becomes the pen
Of him that writeth things divine to men :
But must I needs want solidness, because
By metaphors I speak ? Were not God's laws,
His gospel laws, in olden time held forth
By shadows, types, and metaphors ? Yet loath
Will any sober man be to find fault
With them, lest he be found for to assault
The Highest Wisdom. No ; he rather stoops,
And seeks to find out what by pins and loops,
By calves and sheep, by heifers and by rams,
By birds and herbs, and by the blood of lambs
God speaketh to him ; and happy is he
That finds the light and grace that in them be.

Be not too forward, therefore, to conclude
That I want solidness, that I am rude :
All things solid in show, not solid be :
All things in parable despise not we,
Lest things most hurtful lightly we receive,
And things that good are, of our souls bereave.
My dark and cloudy words, they do but hold
The truth, as cabinets enclose the gold.

The prophers used much by metaphors
To set forth truth; yea whoso considers
Christ, His apostles too, shall plainly see
The truths to this day in such mantles be.

Am I afraid to say that Holy Writ,
Which for its style and phrase puts down all wit,
Is everywhere so full of all these things
(Dark figures, allegories)? yet there springs
From that same book that lustre, and those rays
Of light, that turn our darkest nights to days.

Come, let my carper to his life now look,
And find there darker linest han in my book
He findeth any; yea, and let him know,
That in his best things there are worse lines too.

May we but stand before impartial men,
To his poor one I dare adventure ten
That they will take my meaning in these lines
Far better than his lies in silver shrines.
Come, Truth, although in swaddling-clouts I find,
Informs the judgment, rectifies the mind;
Pleases the understanding, makes the will
Submit; the memory, too, it doth fill
With what both our imagination please;
Likewise it tends our troubles to appease.

Sound words, I know, Timothy is to use,
And old wives' fables he is to refuse;
But yet grave Paul him nowhere did forbid
The use of parables, in which lay hid
That gold, those pearls, and precious stones that were
Worth digging for, and that with greatest care.

Let me add one word more: Oh, man of God!
Art thou offended? Dost thou wish I had
Put forth my matter in another dress?
Or that I had in things been more express?
To those that are my betters, as is fit,
Three things let me propound, then I submit:

1. I find not that I am denied the use
Of this my method, so I no abuse
Put on the words, things, readers, or be rude
In handling figure or similitude
In application; but all that I may
Seek the advance of truth, this or that way.
Denied, did I say? Nay, I have leave
(Examples too, and that from them that have
God better pleased, by their words or ways,
Than any man that breatheth nowadays)
Thus to express my mind, thus to declare
Things unto thee that excellentest are.

2. I find that men (as high as trees) will write
Dialogue-wise; yet no man doth them slight
For writing so; indeed, if they abuse
Truth, cursed be they, and the craft they use
To that intent; but yet let truth be free
To make her sallies upon thee and me,
Which way it pleases God; for who knows how
Better than He that taught us first to plough,
To guide our minds and pens for His design?
And He makes base things usher in Divine.

3. I find that Holy Writ, in many places,
Hath semblance with this method, where the cases
Do call for one thing to set forth another:
Use it I may then, and yet nothing smother
Truth's golden beams: nay, by this method may
Make it cast forth its rays as light as day.

And now, before I do put up my pen,
I'll show the profit of my book, and then
Commit both me and it unto that Hand
That pulls the strong down, and makes weak ones stand.

This book, it chalketh out before thine eyes
The man that seeks the everlasting prize:
It shows you whence he comes, whither he goes;
What he leaves undone: also what he does;

It also shows you how he runs and runs,
Till he unto the Gate of Glory comes.
It shows, too, who set out for life amain,
As if the lasting crown they would obtain.
Here also you may see the reason why
They lose their labor, and like fools do die.

This book will make a traveller of thee,
If by its counsel thou wilt ruled be;
It will direct thee to the Holy Land,
If thou wilt its direction understand;
Yea, it will make the slothful active be;
The blind also delightful things to see.

Art thou for something rare and profitable,
Or wouldst thou see a truth within a fable?
Art thou forgetful? Wouldst thou remember
From New-year's day to the last of December?
Then read my fancies; they will stick like burs,
And may be to the helpless comforters.

This book is writ in such a dialect
As may the minds of listless men affect;
It seems a novelty, and yet contains
Nothing but sound and honest gospel strains.

Wouldst thou divert thyself from melancholy?
Wouldst thou be pleasant, yet be far from folly?
Wouldst thou read riddles and their explanation,
Or else be drowned in thy contemplation?
Dost thou love picking meat? Or wouldst thou see
A man i' the clouds, and hear him speak to thee?
Wouldst thou be in a dream and yet not sleep?
Or wouldst thou in a moment laugh and weep?
Wouldst thou lose thyself and catch no harm,
And find thyself again without a charm?
Wouldst read thyself, and read thou knowest not what,
And yet know whether thou art blest or not,
By reading the same lines? Oh, then, come hither,
And lay my book, thy head, and heart together.

JOHN BUNYAN.

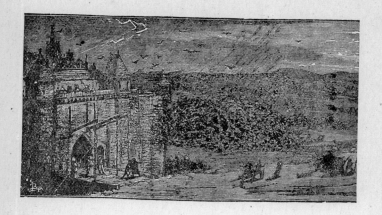

THE PILGRIM'S PROGRESS.

AS I walked through the wilderness of this world, I lighted on a certain place where was a Den, and I laid me down in that place to sleep ; and, as I slept, I dreamed a dream. I dreamed I saw a man clothed with rags, standing in a certain place, with his face from his own house, a book in his hand, and a great burden upon his back. I looked, and saw him open the book, and read therein ; and, as he read, he wept and trembled ; and, not being able longer to contain he brake out with a lamentable cry, saying, "What shall I do ?"

In this plight, therefore, he went home and refrained himself as long as he could, that his wife and children should not perceive his distress ; but he could not be silent long, because that his trouble increased. Where fore at length he brake his mind to his wife and children ; and thus he began to talk to them : O my dear wife, said he, and you my children, I am undone by reason of a burden that lieth hard upon me ; moreover, I am for certain informed that this our city will be burned with fire from heaven ; in which fearful overthrow, both myself, with thee, my wife, and you, my sweet babes. shall miserably come to ruin, except some way of escape can be found. At this his relations were sore amazed ; not for that they believed that what he said to them was true, but because they thought that some frenzy distemper had got into his head ; therefore, it drawing towards night, and they hoping that sleep might settle his brains, with all haste they got him to bed. But the night was as troublesome to him as the day ; wherefore, instead of sleeping, he spent it in sighs and tears. So, when the morning was come, they asked how he did. He told them, Worse and worse : and set to talking to them again ; but they began to be hardened. The also thought to drive away his distemper by harsh and surly carriages to him ; sometimes they would deride, sometimes chide, and sometimes they would quite neglect him. Wherefore he began to retire himself to his chamber, to pray for and pity them, and also to condole his own misery ; he would also walk solitarily in the fields, sometimes reading and sometimes praying : and thus for some days he spent his time.

Now, I saw, when he was walking in the fields, that he was reading in his book, and greatly distressed in his mind ; and, as he read, he burst out, as he had done before, crying, "What shall I do to be saved ?"

I saw also that he looked this way and that way, as if he would run ; yet he stood still, because, as I perceived, he could not tell in which way to go. I looked then, and saw a man named Evangelist coming to him, who asked, Wherefore dost thou cry?

He answered, Sir, I perceive by the book in my hand, that I am condemned to die, and after that to come to judgment; and I find that I am not willing to do the first, nor able to do the second.

Then said Evangelist, Why not willing to die, since this life is attended with so many evils? The man answered, Because I fear that this burden that is upon my back will sink me lower than the grave, and I shall fall into Tophet. And, Sir, if I be not fit to go to prison, I am not fit, I am sure, to go to judgment, and from thence to execution; and the thought of these things make me cry.

HE BEGAN TO PRAY.

Then said Evangelist, If this be by condition, why standest thou still? He answered, Because I know not whither to go. Then he gave him a parchment roll, and there was written within. Flee from the wrath to come.

The man, therefore, read it, and looking upon Evangelist very carefully, said, Whither must I fly?

Then said Evangelist, pointing with his finger over a very wide field, Do you see yonder wicket-gate? The man said, No. Then said the other, Do you see yonder shining light? He said, I think I do. Then said Evangelist, Keep that light in your eye, and go up directly thereto; so shalt thou see the gate; at which, when thou knockest, it shall be told thee what thou shalt do. So I saw in my dream that the man began to run. Now, he had not run far from his own door, but his wife and children, perceiving it, began to cry after him to return; but the man put his fingers in his ears, and ran on crying, Life! life! eternal life! So he looked not behind him, but fled towards the middle of the plain.

PLIABLE.

The neighbors also came out to see him run, and, as he ran, some mocked, others threatened, and some cried after him to return; and, among those that did so, there were two that resolved to fetch him back by force. The name of the one was Obstinate, and the name of the other was Pliable. Now, by this time, the man was a good distance from them; but they pursued him, and in a little time they overtook him. Then said the man, Neighbors, where-fore are ye come? They said, To persuade you to go back with us. But he said, That can by no means be; you dwell in the City of Destruction, the place where I also was born; I see it to be so; and, dying there, sooner or later, you will sink lower than the grave, into a place that burns with fire and brimstone; be content, good neigh-bors, and go along with me.

OBSTINATE. What! and leave our friends and our comforts be-hind us?

Yes, said Christian, for that was his name, because that ALL which you shall forsake is not worthy to be compared with a little of that which I am seeking to enjoy, and if you will go along with me, you shall fare as I myself; for there where I go, is

OBSTINATE.

enough and to spare. Come away and prove my words.

OBSTINATE. What are the things you seek, since you leave all the world to find them?

CHRISTIAN. I seek an inheritance incorruptible, undefiled; and that fadeth not away, and it is laid up safe in heaven, to be bestowed, at the time appointed, on them that diligently seek it. Read it so, if you will, in my book.

OBSTINATE. Tush! away with your book; will you go back with us or no?

CHRISTIAN. No, not I, because I have laid my hand to the plough.

OBSTINATE. Come, then, neighbor Pliable, let us turn and go home without him; there is a company of these crazy-headed coxcombs, that, when they take a fancy, are wiser in their own eyes than seven men that can render a reason.

PLIABLE. Then, don't revile; if what good Christian says is true, the things he looks after are better than ours; my heart inclines to go with my neighbor.

OBSTINATE. What! more fools still! Be ruled by me, and go back; who knows whither such a brain-sick fellow will lead you? Go back, go back, and be wise.

CHRISTIAN. Nay, but do thou come with thy neighbor Pliable; there are to be had such things as I spoke of, and many more glories besides. If you believe me not, read in this book; and for the truth of what is expressed therein, behold, all is confirmed by the blood of Him that made it.

PLIABLE. Well, neighbor Obstinate, I begin to come to a point; I intend to go along and cast my lot with this good man; but, my good companion, do you know the way to this desired place?

CHRISTIAN. I am directed by a man, whose name is Evangelist, to speed me to a little gate that is before us, where we shall receive instructions about the way.

PLIABLE. Come, then, good neighbor, let us be going. Then they went together

OBSTINATE. And I will go back to my place. I will be no companion of such misled, fantastical fellows.

Now, I saw in my dream, that, when Obstinate was gone back, Christian and Pliable went talking over the plain; and thus they began their discourse.

CHRISTIAN. Come, neighbor Pliable, how do you do? I am glad you are persuaded to go along with me. Had even Obstinate himself but felt what I have felt of the powers and terrors of what is yet unseen, he would not thus lightly have given us the back.

PLIABLE. Come, neighbor Christian, since there are none but us two here, tell me now further what the things are, and how to be enjoyed, whither we are going.

CHRISTIAN. I can better conceive of them with my mind, than speak of them with my tongue, but yet, since you are desirous to know, I will read of them in my book.

PLIABLE. And do you think that the words of your book are certainly true?

CHRISTIAN. Yes, verily; for it was made by Him that cannot lie.

PLIABLE. Well said; what things are they?

CHRISTIAN. There is an endless kingdom to be inhabited, and everlasting life to be given us, that we may inhabit that kingdom forever.

PLIABLE. Well said; and what else?

CHRISTIAN. There are crowns of glory to be given us, and garments that will make us shine like the sun in the firmament of heaven.

PLIABLE. This is very pleasant; and what else?

CHRISTIAN. There shall be no more crying, nor sorrow; for he that is owner of the place will wipe all tears from our eyes

PLIABLE.   And what company shall we have there?

CHRISTIAN.   There we shall be with seraphims and cherubims, creatures that will dazzle your eyes to look on them.   There also you shall meet with thousands and ten thousands that have gone before us, none of them are hurtful, but loving and holy; every one walking in the sight of God, and in his presence with acceptance for ever.   In a word, there we shall see the elders with their golden crowns; there we shall see the holy virgins with their golden harps; there we shall see men that by the world were cut in pieces, burnt in flames, eaten of beasts, drowned in the seas, for the love that they bare to the Lord of the place, all well, and clothed with immorality as with a garment.

PLIABLE.   The hearing of this is enough to ravish one's heart.   But are these things to be enjoyed?   How shall we get to be sharers thereof?

CHRISTIAN.   The Lord, the Governor of the country, hath recorded that in this book; the substance of which is, If we be truly willing to have it, he will bestow it upon us freely.

PLIABLE.   Well, my good companion, glad am I to hear of these things; come on, let us mend our pace.

CHRISTIAN.   I cannot go so fast as I would, by reason of this burden that is on my back.

Now, I saw in my dream, that just as they had ended this talk they drew near to a very miry slough, that was in the midst of the plain; and they, being heedless, did both fall suddenly into the bog.   The name of the slough was Despond.   Here, therefore, they wallowed for a time, being grievously bedaubed with dirt; and Christian, because of the burden that was on his back began to sink in the mire.

PLIABLE.   Ah! neighbor Christian, where are you now?

Truly, said Christian, I do not know.

PLIABLE.   At this Pliable began to be offended, and angrily said to his fellow, Is this the happiness you have told me all this while of ? If we have such ill speed at our first setting out, what may we expect betwixt this and our journey's end ?   May I get out again with my life, you shall possess the brave country alone. And, with that, he gave a desperate struggle or two, and got out of the mire on the side next to his own house ; so away he went, and Christian saw him no more.

Wherefore Christian was left to tumble in the Slough of Despond alone ; but still he endeavored to struggle to that side that was still further from his own house, and next to the wicket-gate ; the which he did, but could not get out because of the burden that was upon his back ; but I beheld in my dream, that a man came to him, whose name was Help, and asked him, What he did there ?

CHRISTIAN.   Sir, I was bid go this way by a man called Evangelist, who directed me also to yonder gate, that I might escape the wrath to come ; and as I was going thither I fell in here.

HELP.   But why did not you look for the steps ?

CHRISTIAN.   Fear followed me so hard, that I fled the next way, and fell in.

Help then gave him his hand, and he drew him out, and set him upon sound ground, and bid him go on his way.

Then I stepped to him that plucked him out, and said, Sir, since over this place is the way from the City of Destruction to yonder gate, why is it that this plat is not mended, that poor travellers might go thither with more security ?   And he said unto me, This miry slough is such a place as cannot be mended ; it is the descent whither the scum and filth that attends conviction for sin doth continually run, and therefore it is called the Slough of Despond ; for still, as the sinner is awakened about his lost condition, there ariseth in his soul many fears, and doubts and discouragements, all of which get together, and settle in this place. And this is the reason of the badness of this ground. It is not the pleasure of the King that this place should remain so bad. His laborers have, by the direction of His Majesty's surveyors, been for over sixteen hundred years employed about this patch of ground, if perhaps it might be mended : yea, and to my knowledge, here have been swallowed up at least twenty thousand cartloads, yea, millions of good instructions, that have been brought from all places of the King's dominions, and they say they are the best materials to make good ground of the place, if so be it might have been mended ; but it is the Slough of Despond still, and so will be when they have done what they can.

True, there are, by the direction of the Lawgiver, certain good and substantial steps, placed even through the very midst of this slough ; but as this place doth much spew out its filth, as it doth at change of weather, these steps are hardly seen ; and men, through the dizziness of their heads, step beside, and are bemired notwithstanding the steps be there ; but the ground is good when they are once in the gate.

Now, I saw in my dream, that by this time Pliable was got home to his house again, so that his neighbors came to visit him ; and some of them called him wise man for coming back, and some called him fool for hazarding himself with Christian ; others again did mock at his cowardliness saying, Surely, since you began to venture, I would not have been so base to have given out for a few difficulties.   So Pliable sat sneaking among them.   But at last he got more confidence, and then they all turned their tales, and began to deride poor Christian behind his back.

Now, as Christian was walking by himself, he espied one afar off, come crossing over the field to meet him ; and their hap was to meet just as they were crossing the way of each other.   The gentleman's name was Mr. Wordly Wiseman ; he dwelt in the town of Carnal Policy, a very great town, hardby from whence Christian came.   This man then, meeting with Christian, and having heard of his setting forth from the City of Destruction, as it was much noised abroad, not only in the town where he dwelt, but, also it began to be the town talk in some other places.   Mr. Worldly Wiseman, beholding his laborious going, and observing his sighs and groans, and the like, began thus to enter into some talk with Christian.

WORLDLY.   How now, good fellow, whither away after this burdened manner ?

CHRISTIAN.   A burdened manner, indeed, as ever. poor creature had !   And whereas you ask me, Whither away ?   I tell you, Sir, I am going to yonder wicket-gate before me ; for there, as I am informed, I shall be put into a way to get rid of my heavy burden.

WORLDLY.   Hast thou a wife and children ?

CHRISTIAN.   Yes ; but I am so ladden with this burden, that I cannot take that pleasure in them as formerly ; methinks I am as if I had none.

WORLDLY.   Wilt thou hearken unto me if I give thee counsel ?

CHRISTIAN.   If it be good, I will ; for I stand in need of good counsel.

WORLDLY.   I would advise thee, then, that thou with
all speed get rid of thy burden ; for thou wilt never be

WORLDLY WISEMAN.

settled in thy mind till then ; nor canst thou enjoy the
benefits of the blessing which God has bestowed upon
thee till then.

CHRISTIAN. I seek to be rid of this heavy burden, but get it off myself, I cannot ; nor is there any man in our country that can take it off my shoulders ; so I am going this way, as I told you, that I may be rid of it.

WORLDLY. Who bid thee go this way to be rid of thy burden ?

CHRISTIAN. A man that appeared to me to be a very great and honorable person ; his name, as I remember, is Evangelist.

WORLDLY. I beshrew him for his counsel ! there is not a more dangerous and troublesome way in the world than is that unto which he hath directed thee ; and that thou shalt find, if thou wilt be ruled by his counsel. Thou hast met with something, as I perceive, already ; for I see the dirt of the Slough of Despond is upon thee ; but that slough is the beginning of the sorrows that do attend those that go on in that way. Hear me, I am older than thou ; thou art like to meet with, in the way which thou goest, weariness, pain, hunger, perils, nakedness, sword, lions, dragons, darkness, and death. These things are certainly true, having been confirmed by many testimonies. And why should a man so carelessly cast away himself, by giving heed to a stranger ?

CHRISTIAN. Why, Sir, this burden upon my back is more terrible to me than are all these things which you have mentioned ; nay, methinks I care not what I meet with in the way, if so be I can also meet with deliverance from my burden.

WORLDLY. How camest thou by the burden at first ?

CHRISTIAN. By reading this book in my hand.

WORLDLY. I thought so ; and it is happened unto thee as to other weak men, who, meddling with things too high for them, do suddenly fall into distractions which do not only unman men, as thine, I perceive, has done thee, but run them upon desperate ventures to obtain they know not what.

CHRISTIAN. I know what I would obtain ; it is ease from my heavy burden.

WORLDLY. Hadst thou but patience to hear me, I could direct thee to the obtaining of what thou desirest, without the dangers thou wilt run thyself into ; yea, and the remedy is at hand. Besides, instead of those dangers, thou shalt meet with safety, friendship, and content.

CHRISTIAN. Pray, Sir, open this secret to me.

WORLDLY. Why, in yonder village, named Morality, there dwells a gentleman whose name is Legality, a very judicious man, and a man of a very good name, that has skill to help men off with such burdens as thine ; yea, to my knowledge, he hath done a great deal of good this way ; ay, and he hath skill to cure those that are somewhat crazed in their wits with their burdens. To him go and be helped presently. His house is not quite a mile from this place, and if he should not be at home himself, he hath a pretty young man to his son, whose name is Civility, that can do it as well as the old gentleman himself ; there, I say, thou mayest be eased of thy burden ; and if thou art not minded to go back to thy former habitation, as, indeed, I would not wish thee, thou mayest send for thy wife and children to thee to this village, where there are houses now empty, one of which thou mayest have at reasonable rates ; provision is there also cheap and good ; and that which will make thy life the more happy is, to be sure, there thou shalt live by honest neighbors, in credit and good fashion.

Now was Christian somewhat to a stand ; but pres-

ently he concluded, If this be true, which this gentleman hath said, my wisest course is to take his advice;
and with that he thus further spoke, Sir, which is my
way to this honest man's house?

WORLDLY.   Do you see yonder hill?   As you go by
it the first house you come to is his.

So Christian turned out of his way to go to Mr.
Legality's house for help; but, behold, when he was
got now hard-by the hill, it seemed so high, and also
that side of it that was next the wayside, did hang so
much over, that Christian was afraid to venture further,
lest the hill should fall on his head; wherefore there he
stood still, and knew not what to do.   His burden now
seemed heavier to him than before.   There came also
flashes of fire out of the hill, that made Christian sweat
and quake for fear that he should be burned.

And now he began to be sorry that he had taken
Worldly Wiseman's counsel.   Then he saw Evangelist
coming to meet him; at the sight of whom he began to
blush for shame.   Evangelist drew nearer; and coming up to him, looked upon him with a severe countenance, and thus began to reason with Christian.

EVANGELIST.   What dost thou here, Christian?   Which
words Christian knew not what to answer, and stood
speechless before him.   Then said Evangelist. Art
not thou the man that I found crying without the walls
of the City of Destruction?

CHRISTIAN.   Yes, dear Sir, I am the man.

EVANGELIST.   Did I not direct the way to the little
wicket-gate?

CHRISTIAN.   Yes, dear Sir.

EVANGELIST.   How is it then, that thou art so quickly turned aside? for thou art now out of the way.

CHRISTIAN   I met with a gentleman so soon as I had

got over the Slough of Despond, who persuaded me that I might, in yonder village, find a man that could take off my burden. He looked like a gentleman, and talked much to me, and got me at last to yield ; so I came hither ; but when I beheld this hill, and how it hangs over the way, I suddenly made a stand lest it should fall on my head.

EVANGELIST. What said that gentleman to you?

CHRISTIAN. Why, he asked me whither I was going? And I told him. He asked me if I had a family? And I told him. But, said I, I am so loaden with the burden that is on my back, that I cannot take pleasure in them as formerly. He also bid me with speed get rid of my burden ; and I told him it was ease that I sought. And, said I, I am therefore going to yonder gate, to receive further direction how I may get to the place of deliverance. So he said that he would show me a better way, and short, not so attended with difficulties as the way, Sir, that you set me in ; which way, said he, will direct you to a gentleman's house that hath skill to take off these burdens, so I believed him, and turned out of that way into this. But when I came to this place, and beheld things as they are, I stopped for fear of danger; but I now know not what to do.

Then, said Evangelist, stand still a little, that I may show thee the words of God. So he stood trembling. Then said Evangelist, "See that ye refuse not him that speaketh. For if they escaped not who refused him that spake on earth, much more *shall not* we *escape*, if we turn away from him that *speaketh* from heaven. Now the just shall live by faith : but if *any man* draw back, my soul shall have no pleasure in him." He also did thus apply them : Thou art the man that art running into this misery ; thou hast begun to reject the counsel of the Most High, and to draw back thy foot from the way of peace, even almost to the hazarding of thy perdition.

Then Christian fell down at his feet as dead, crying, "Woe is me, for I am undone !" At the sight of which, Evangelist caught him by the right hand, saying, "All manner of sin and blasphemy shall be forgiven unto men. Be not faithless, but believing." Then Christian revived a little and stood up trembling as before.

Then Evangelist said, Give more earnest heed to the things that I tell thee of. I will now show thee who it was that deluded thee, and who it was also to whom he sent thee. The man that met thee is one Worldly Wiseman, so called because he savoreth only the doctrine of this world, and because he loveth that doctrine best, for it saveth him best from the cross. And as he is of this carnal temper, he seeketh to prevent my ways though right. Now, there are three things in this man's counsel that thou must utterly abhor.

(1) His turning thee out of the way. (2) His laboring to render the cross odious to thee. And (3) His setting thy feet in that way that leadeth unto death.

First, thou must abhor his turning thee out of the way, and thine own consenting thereto ; because this is to reject the counsel of God for the sake of the counsel of a Worldly Wiseman. The Lord says, " Strive to enter in at the strait gate," the gate to which I send thee ; for "strait is the gate that leadeth unto life, and few there be that find it." From this little wicket-gate, and from the way thereto, hath this wicked man turned thee, to the bringing of thee almost to destruction.

hate, therefore, his turning thee out of the way, and abhor thyself for hearkening to him.

Secondly, thou must abhor his laboring to render the cross odious unto thee ; for thou art to prefer it "before the treasures in Egypt." Besides, the King of glory hath told thee, that he that "will save his life shall lose it." And, "He that cometh after me, and hateth not his father, and mother, and wife, and children, and brethren, and sisters, yea, and his own life also, he cannot be my disciple." I say, therefore, if man persuade thee, that that shall be thy death, without which, THE TRUTH hath said, thou canst not have eternal life ; this doctrine thou must abhor.

Thirdly, Thou must hate his setting of thy feet in the way that leadeth to death. And for this thou must consider to whom he sent thee, and also how unable that person was to deliver thee from thy burden.

He to whom thou was sent for ease, by name Legality, is the son of the bondwoman which now is in bondage with her children ; and is, in a mystery, this Mount Sinai, which thou hast feared will fall on thy head. Now, if she, with her children, are in bondage, how canst thou expect by them to be made free? This Legality, therefore, is not able to set thee free from thy burden. No man was as yet ever rid of his burden by him ; no, nor ever is like to be : ye cannot be justified by the works of the law ; therefore, Worldly Wiseman is an alien, and Legality is a cheat ; and his son Civility is but a hypocrite and cannot help thee. Believe me, there is nothing in all this noise, that thou hast heard of these sottish men, but a design to beguile thee of thy salvation, by turning thee from the way in which I had set thee. After this, Evangelist called aloud to the heavens for confirmation of what he had said : and with that there came words and fire out of the mountain under which poor Christian stood, that made his hair stand up. The words were thus pronounced : "As many as are of the works of the law are under the curse ; for it is written, Cursed is every one that continueth not in all things which are written in the book of the law to do them."

Now Christian looked for nothing but death, and began to cry lamentably ; cursing the time he met Worldly Wiseman, calling himself a thousand fools for hearkening to his counsel ; he also was greatly ashamed to think that this gentleman's arguments, flowing only from the flesh, should cause him to forsake the right way. This done, he applied himself again to Evangelist.

CHRISTIAN. Sir, what think you ? Is there hope ? May I now go back to the wicket-gate ? Shall I not be abandoned, and sent back ashamed ? I am sorry I have hearkened to this man's counsel. But may my sin be forgiven ?

EVANGELIST. Thy sin is very great, for thou hast committed two evils : thou hast forsaken the way that is good, to tread in forbidden paths ; yet will the man at the gate receive thee, for he has good-will for men ; only, take heed that thou turn not aside again, "lest thou perish from the way, when his wrath is kindled but a little."

Then did Christian decide to go back ; and Evangelist kissed him, gave him one smile, and bid him God-speed. So he went on with haste, neither spake he to any man by the way ; nor, if any asked him, would he vouchsafe them an answer. He went on like one that was treading on forbidden ground, and could by no means think himself safe, till again he was got into the way which he left. So Christian got up to the gate. Now, over the gate was written, "Knock, and it shall be opened unto you." He knocked, therefore, more than once or twice.

CHRISTIAN GETS A PULL AS HE WAS STEPPING IN.

At last there came to the gate a grave person named Goodwill, who asked who was there? and whence he came? and what he would have?

CHRISTIAN. Here is a poor burdened sinner. I come from the City of Destruction, but am going to Mount Zion, that I may be delivered from the wrath to come. I would therefore ask, Sir, since I am informed that this gate is the way thither, if you are willing to let me in?

GOOD-WILL. I am willing with all my heart, said he; and with that he opened the gate.

So when Christian was stepping in, the other gave him a pull. Then said Christian, What means that? The other told him. A little distance from the gate, there is a castle, of which Beelzebub is the captain, and he and them that are with him shoot arrows at those who come up to this gate, if haply they may die before they can enter in.

Then said Christian, I rejoice and tremble. When he was got in, the man of the gate asked him who directed him thither?

CHRISTIAN. Evangelist bid me come and knock ; and that you, Sir, would tell me what I must do.

GOOD-WILL. But how is it that you came alone ?

CHRISTIAN. Because none of my neighbors saw their danger as I saw mine.

GOOD-WILL. Did any of them know of your coming ?

CHRISTIAN. Yes ; my wife and children saw me at the first, and called after me to turn again ; also some of my neighbors stood crying after me to return ; but I put my fingers in my ears, and came on my way.

GOOD-WILL. But did none of them follow you to persuade you to go back ?

CHRISTIAN. Yes, both Obstinate and Pliable ; but when they saw that they could not prevail, Obstinate went railing back, but Pliable came with me a little way, until we came to the Slough of Despond, into the which we suddenly fell. And then Pliable was discouraged, and would not adventure further. Wherefore, getting out again on that side next to his own house, he told me I should possess the brave country alone ; so he went his way, and I came mine.

GOOD-WILL. Alas, poor man ! is the celestial glory of so small esteem with him, that he counteth it not worth running the hazards of a few difficulties to obtain it ?

CHRISTIAN. Truly, I have said the truth of Pliable,

The Pilgrim's Progress—2.

"HE WAS A TALL MAN."

See page 90.

and if I should also say all the truth to myself, it will appear there is no betterment betwixt him and myself. It is true, he went back to his own house, but I also turned aside to go in the way of death, being persuaded thereto by the carnal arguments of one Worldly Wiseman.

GOOD-WILL. Oh, did he light upon you and did you take his counsel?

CHRISTIAN. Yes, as far as I durst; I went to find out Legality, until I thought the mountain that stands by his house would have fallen upon my head; wherefore I was forced to stop.

GOOD-WILL. That mountain has been the death of many, and will be the death of many more; it is well you escaped being by it dashed in pieces.

BEELZEBUB SHOOTING ARROWS.

CHRISTIAN. Why, truly, I do not know what had become of me there, had not Evangelist happily met me again, as I was musing in the midst of my dumps; but it was God's mercy that he came to me again, for else I had never come hither. But now I am come, such a one as I am; more fit, indeed, for death by that mountain than thus to stand talking with my Lord; but, oh, what a favor is this to me, that yet I am admitted here!

GOOD-WILL. We make no objections against any, notwithstanding all that they have done before they came hither. They are "in no wise cast out," and therefore, good Christian, come a little way with me, and I will teach thee about the way thou must go. Look before thee; dost thou see this norrow way? THAT is the way thou must go; it was cast up by patriarchs, prophets, Christ and his apostles; and it is as straight as a rule can make it. This is the way thou must go.

CHRISTIAN. But, are there no turnings or windings, by which a stranger may lose his way?

GOOD-WILL. Yes, there are many ways leading from this, and they are crooked and wide. But thou mayest distinguish the right from the wrong, the right only being straight and narrow.

Then I saw in my dream, that Christian asked him further if he could not help him off with his burden that was upon his back; for as yet he had not got rid thereof, nor could he by any means get it off without help. He told him, As to thy burden be content to bear it, until thou comest to the place of deliverance; for there it will fall from thy back of itself.

Then Christian girded up his loins, and prepared for his journey. So the other told him, that some distance from the gate he would come to the house of the Interpreter, at whose door he should knock, and he would show him excellent things. Then Christian took leave of his friend, bidding him God-speed. Then he went on to the house of the Interpreter, where he knocked until one came to the door, and asked who was there.

CHRISTIAN. Sir, here is a traveller, who was bid by an acquaintance of the good master of this house to call here and speak with him. So the master of the house after a little time came to Christian, and asked him what he would have. Sir, said Christian, I am come from the City of Destruction, and am going to the Mount Zion. I was told that if I called here, you would show me excellent things, such as would be a help to me in my journey.

INTERPRETER. Come in; I will show that which will be profitable to thee. So he commanded his man to light the candle, and bid Christian follow him into a private room where Christian saw the picture of a very grave person hang up against the wall. It had eyes lifted up to heaven, the best of books in his hands, the law of truth was written upon his lips, the world was behind his back. It stood as if it pleaded with men, and a crown of gold did hang over his head.

Then said Christian, what meaneth this.?

INTERPRETER. This picture is to show thee that this man's work is to know and unfold dark things to sinners; even as thou seest him stand as if he pleaded with men; and whereas thou seest the world as cast behind him, and that a crown hangs over his head, that is to show thee that, slighting and despising the things that are present for the love that he hath to his Master's service, he is sure in the world that comes next to have glory for his reward. Now, I have showed thee this picture first, because the man whose picture this is, is the only man whom the Lord of the place, whither thou art going, hath authorized to be thy guide in all difficult places thou mayest meet with in the way ; wherefore take good heed to what I have showed thee, and bear well in thy mind what thou hast seen, lest in thy journey thou meet with some that pretend to lead thee right, but their way goes down to death.

Then he took him by the hand, and led him into a very large parlor that was full of dust, because never swept ; the Interpreter called for a man to sweep. Now, when he began to sweep, the dust began so abundantly to fly about, that Christian had almost therewith been choked. Then said the Interpreter to a damsel that stood by, Bring hither the water and sprinkle the room. When she had done this it was swept and cleansed with pleasure.

CHRISTIAN. What means this ?

The Interpreter answered, This parlor is the heart of a man that was never sanctified by the sweet grace of the gospel ; the dust is his original sin and inward corruptions, that have defiled the whole man. He that began to sweep at first, is the Law ; but she that brought water, and did sprinkle it, is the Gospel. Now, whereas thou sawest, that so soon as the first began to sweep, the dust did so fly about that the room by him could not be cleansed, but that thou wast almost choked therewith ; this is to show thee, that the law, instead of cleansing the heart (by its working) from sin, doth revive, put strength into, and increase it in the soul, even as it doth discover and forbid it, for it doth not give power to subdue.

Again, as thou sawest the damsel sprinkle the room with water, upon which it was cleansed with pleasure ; this is to show thee, that when the gospel comes, in the sweet and precious influences thereof, to the heart, then as the damsel laid the dust by sprinkling the floor with water, so is sin vanquished and subdued, and the soul made clean through the faith of it, and consequently fit for the King of glory to inhabit.

I saw, moreover, in my dream, that the Interpreter took him by the hand, and had him into a little room, where sat two little children, each one in his chair. The name of the eldest was Passion, and the name of the other Patience. Passion seemed to be much discontented ; but Patience was very quiet. Then Christian asked, What is the reason of the discontent of Passion ? The Interpreter answered, The Governor would have him stay for his best things till the beginning of the next year ; but he will have all now ; but Patience is willing to wait. Then I saw that one came to Passion, and brought him a bag of treasure, and poured it down at his feet, which he took up and rejoiced therein, and withal laughed Patience to scorn. But I beheld but a while, and he had lavished all away, and nothing left him but rags.

CHRISTIAN. Expound this matter more fully to me.

INTERPRETER. So he said, These two lads are symbols. Passion, of the men of this world ; and Patience, of the men of that which is to come ; for as here thou seest, Passion will have his all this year, that is to say, in this world ; so are the men of this world : they must have all their good things now. The proverb, " A bird in the hand is worth two in the bush," is of more authority with them than are all the Divine testimonies of the good of the world to come. But as thou sawest that he had quickly lavished all away, and had presently left him nothing but rags ; so will it be with all such men at the end of this world.

CHRISTIAN. Now I see that Patience has the best wisdom, and that upon many accounts. First, because he stays for the best things. Second, because he will have the glory of his when the other has nothing but rags.

INTERPRETER. Nay, you may add another; to wit, the glory of the next world will never wear out, but these are suddenly gone. Therefore Passion had not so much reason to laugh at Patience, because he had his good things first, as Patience will have to laugh at Passion, because he had his best things last ; for first must give place to last, because last must have his time to come ; but last gives place to nothing ; for there is not another to succeed. He, therefore, that hath his portion first, must needs have a time to spend it ; but he that hath his portion last, must have it lastingly ; therefore it is said of Dives, "Thou in thy lifetime receivedst thy good things, and likewise Lazarus evil things ; but now he is comforted, and thou art tormented."

Then I saw in my dream that the Interpreter took Christian by the hand, and led him into a place where was a fire burning against the wall, and one standing by it, always casting much water upon it, to quench it ; yet did the fire burn higher and hotter.

Then said Christian, What means this ?

The Interpreter answered, This fire is the work of grace that is wrought in the heart ; he that casts water upon it to extinguish and put it out, is the Devil ; but notwithstanding that the fire burns higher and hotter. Thou shalt also see the reason of that. So he turned about to the back side of the wall, where he saw a man with a vessel of oil in his hand, which oil he did continually cast secretly into the fire.

CHRISTIAN. What means this ?

INTERPRETER. This is Christ who continually, with the oil of his grace, maintains the work already begun in the heart ; by means of which, notwithstanding what the Devil can do, the souls of his people prove gracious still. And the man that stood behind the wall to maintain the fire is to teach thee that it is hard for the tempted to see how this work of grace is maintained in the soul.

I saw also, that the Interpreter took him again by the hand, and led him into a pleasant place, where was builded a stately palace, beautiful to behold ; at the sight of which Christian was greatly delighted. He saw also on the top thereof, certain persons walking, who were clothed all in gold.

Then said Christian, May we go in thither ?

Then the Interpreter took him, and led him up towards the palace ; and behold at the door stood a great company of men, as desirous to go in, but durst not. There also sat a man at a little distance from the door, at a tableside, with a book and his inkhorn before him, to take the name of him that should enter therein ; he saw also, that in the doorway stood many men in armor to keep it, being resolved to do the men that would enter what hurt and mischief they could. Now was Christian somewhat in amaze. At last, when every man started back for fear of the armed men, Christian saw a man of a very stout countenance come up to the man that sat there to write, saying, "Set down my name, Sir ;" the which when he had done, he saw the man draw his sword, and put an helmet upon his head, and rush toward the door upon the armed men, who laid upon him with deadly force ; but the man, not at all discouraged, fell to cutting and hacking most fiercely. So after he had received and given many wounds to those that attempted to keep him out, he cut his way through them all, and pressed forward into the palace, at which there was a pleasant voice heard from those within, that walked upon the top of the palace, saying, "Come in, come in, Eternal glory thou shalt win."

So he went in, and was clothed with such garments as they. Then Christian smiled and said, I think verily I know the meaning of this.

Now, said Christian, let me go hence. Nay, stay, said the Interpreter, till I have shown thee a little more, and after that thou shalt go on thy way. So he took him by the hand again, and led him into a very dark room, where there sat a man in an iron cage. Now the man, to look on, seemed very sad ; he sat with his eyes looking down to the ground, his hands folded together, and he sighed as if he would break his heart. Then said Christian, What means this ? At which the Interpreter bid him talk with the man. Then said Christian to the man, What art thou ? The man answered, I am what I was not once.

CHRISTIAN. What wast thou once ?

MAN. I was once a fair and flourishing professor, both in mine own eyes and also in the eyes of others ; I once was, as I thought, fair for the Celestial City, and had joy at the thoughts that I should get thither.

CHRISTIAN. Well, but what art thou now ?

MAN. I am now a man of despair, and am shut up in it, as in this iron cage. I cannot get out. Oh, now I cannot !

CHRISTIAN. But how camest thou in this condition ?

MAN. I left off to watch and be sober ; I laid the reins upon the neck of my lusts ; I sinned against the light of the World and the goodness of God ; I have grieved the Spirit, and he is gone ; I tempted the devil, and he is come to me ; I have provoked God to anger, and he has left me ; I have so hardened my heart, that I cannot repent.

Then said Christian to the Interpreter, But is there no hope for such a man as this ! Ask him, said the Interpreter. Nay, said Christian, pray Sir, do you.

Then said the Interpreter, Is there no hope, but you must be kept in the iron cage of despair ?

MAN. No, none at all.

INTERPRETER. Why, the Son of the blessed is very pitiful.

MAN. *I have crucified him to myself afresh ; I have despised his person ; I have despised his righteousness ; I have "counted his blood an unholy thing ; I have done despite to the Spirit of grace." Therefore I have shut myself out of all the promises, and there now remains to me nothing but threatenings, dreadful threatenings, fearful threatenings of certain judgment and fiery indignation, which shall devour me as an adversary.

INTERPRETER. For what did you bring yourself into this condition ?

MAN. For the lusts, pleasures, and profits of this world ; in the enjoyment of which I did then promise myself much delight ; but now every one of those things also bite me, and gnaw me like a burning worm.

INTERPRETER. But canst thou not now repent and turn ?

MAN. God hath denied me repentance. His Word gives me no encouragement to believe ; yea, himself hath shut me up in this iron cage ; nor can all the men in the world let me out. O eternity, eternity ! how shall I grapple with the misery that I must meet with in eternity !

INTERPRETER. Let this man's misery be remembered by thee, and be an everlasting caution to thee.

CHRISTIAN. Well, this is fearful! God help me to watch and be sober, and to pray that I may shun the cause of this man's misery! Sir, is it not time for me to go on my way now?

INTERPRETER. Tarry till I shall show thee one thing more, and then thou shalt go on thy way.

So he took Christian by the hand again, and led him into a chamber, where there was one rising out of bed; and as he put on his raiment, he shook and trembled. Then said Christian, Why doth this man thus tremble? The Interpreter then bid him tell to Christian the reason of his so doing. So he began and said, This night, as I was in my sleep, I dreamed, and behold the heavens grew exceedingly black; also it thundered and lightened in most fearful wise, that it put me into an agony; so I looked up in my dream, and saw the clouds rack at an unusual rate, upon which I heard a great sound of a trumpet, and saw also a man sit upon a cloud, attended with the thousands of heaven; they were all in flaming fire; also the heavens were in a burning flame. I heard then a voice, saying, "Arise, ye dead, and come to judgment;" and with that the rocks rent, the graves opened, and the dead that were therein came forth. Some of them were exceeding glad, and looked upward; and some sought to hide themselves under the mountains. Then I saw the man that sat upon the cloud open the book, and bid the world draw near. Yet there was, by reason of a fierce flame which issued out and came from before him, a convenient distance betwixt him and them, as betwixt the judge and the prisoners at the bar. I heard it also proclaimed to them that attended on the man that sat on the cloud, "Gather together the tares, the chaff, and stubble, and cast them into the burning lake." And with that the bottomless pit opened, just whereabout I stood ; out of the mouth of which there came, in an abundant manner, smoke and coals of fire, with hideous noises. It was also said to the same persons, "Gather my wheat into the garner." And with that I saw many catched up and carried away into the clouds, but I was left behind. I also sought to hide myself, but I could not, for the man that sat upon the cloud still kept his eye upon me ; my sins also came into my mind ; and my conscience did accuse me on every side. Upon this I awaked from my sleep.

CHRISTIAN. But what was it that made you so afraid of this sight ?

MAN. Why, I thought that the day

THE BOTTOMLESS PIT OPENED JUST WHERE I STOOD.

of judgment was come, and that I was not ready for it ; but this frighted me most, that the angels gathered up several and left me behind ; also the pit of hell opened her mouth just where I stood. My conscience, too, afflicted me ; and, as I thought, the Judge had always his eye upon me, showing indignation in his countenance.

Then said the Interpreter to Christian, Hast thou considered all these things ?

CHRISTIAN. Yes, and they put me in hope and fear.

INTERPRETER. Well, keep all things so in thy mind that they may be as a goad in thy sides, to prick thee forward in the way thou must go.

Then Christian began to gird up his loins, and to address himself to his journey. Then said the Interpreter, The Comforter be always with thee, good Christian, to guide thee in the way that leads to the City. So Christian went on his way.

Now I saw in my dream, that the highway up which Christian was to go, was fenced on either side with a wall, and that wall was called Salvation. Up this way, therefore, did burdened Christian run, but not without great difficulty, because of the load on his back.

He ran thus till he came to a place somewhat ascending, and upon that place stood a cross, and a little below, in the bottom, a sepulchre. So I saw in my dream, that just as Christian came up with the cross, his burden loosed from off his shoulders, and fell from off his back, and began to tumble, and so continued to do till it came to the mouth of the sepulchre, where it fell in, and I saw it no more.

Then was Christian glad and lightsome, and said with a merry heart, "He hath given me rest by his sorrow, and life by his death." Then he stood still a while to look and wonder ; for it was very surprising to him, that the sight of the cross should thus ease him.

of his burden. He looked therefore, and looked again, even till the springs that were in his head sent the waters down his cheeks. Now, as he stood looking and weeping, behold three Shining Ones came to him and saluted him with, "Peace be to thee." So the first said to him, "Thy sins be forgiven thee," the second stripped him of his rags, and clothed him "with change of raiment," the third also set a mark on his forehead, and gave him a roll with a seal upon it, which he bade him look on as he ran, and that he should give it in at the Celestial gate.

Then Christian gave three leaps for joy, and went on singing.

I saw then in my dream, that he went on thus until he came at a bottom, where he saw, a little out of the way, three men fast asleep, with fetters upon their heels. The name of the one was Simple, another Sloth, and the third Presumption.

Christian seeing them lie in this case went to them, if peradventure he might awake them, and cried, You are like them that sleep on the top of a mast, for the Dead Sea is under you — a gulf that hath no bottom. Awake, therefore, and come away; be willing also, and I will help you off with your irons. He also told them, If he that "goeth about like a roaring lion" comes by, will certainly become a pray to his teeth. With that they looked upon him, and began to reply in this sort : Simple said, "I see no danger ;" Sloth said, "Yet a little more sleep ;" and Presumption said, "Every tub must stand upon its own bottom, what is the answer else that I should give thee ?" And so they lay down to sleep again, and Christian went on his way.

Yet was he troubled to think that men in that danger

THE THREE SHINING ONES.

should so little esteem the kindness of him that so freely offered to help them, by awakening them, counselling them, and proffering to help them off with their irons. And as he was troubled thereabout, he espied two men come tumbling over the wall, on the left hand of the narrow way ; and they made up apace to him. The name of the one was Formalist, and the name of the other Hypocrisy. Christian then entered into discourse with them.

CHRISTIAN. Gentlemen, whence came you, and whither go you ?

FORMALIST and HIPOCRISY. We were born in the land of Vainglory, and are going for praise to Mount Zion.

CHRISTIAN. Why came you not in at the gate which standeth at the beginning of the way ? Know you not that it is written, that he that cometh not in by the door, " but climbeth up some other way, the same is a thief and a robber ?"

FORMALIST and HYPOCRISY said, That to go to the gate for entrance was, by all their countrymen, counted too far about ; and that, therefore, their usual way was to make a short cut of it, and to climb over the wall, as they had done.

CHRISTIAN. But will it not be counted a trespass ?

FORMALIST and HYPOCRISY told him then, That he needed not to trouble his head thereabout ; what they did they had custom for and could produce testimony that would witness it for more than a thousand years.

CHRISTIAN. But, will your practice stand a trial at law ?

FORMALIST and HYPOCRISY. That custom, being of so long a standing as above a thousand years, would, doubtless, now be admitted as a thing legal by any impartial judge ; and besides, if we get into the way, what's matter which way we get in? if we are in, we are in ; thou art but in the way, who, as we perceive, came in at the gate; and we are also in the way, that came tumbling over the wall : wherein, now, is thy condition better than ours?

CHRISTIAN. I walk by the rule of my Master ; you walk by the rude working of your fancies. You are counted thieves already by the Lord of the way; therefore, I doubt you will not be found true men at the end. You come in by yourselves, without his direction ; and shall go out by yourselves, without his mercy.

To this they made him but little answer ; only they bid him look to himself. Then I saw that they went on every man in his way, without much conference one with another ; save that these two men told Christian, that, as to

FORMALIST.

laws and ordinances, they doubted not but they should as conscientiously do them as he ; therefore, said they, we see not wherein thou differest from us but by the coat that is on thy back, which was, as we trow, given thee by some of thy neighbors, to hide the shame of thy nakedness.

HYPOCRISY.

By laws and ordinances you will not be saved, since you came not in by the door. And as for this coat that is on my back, it was given me by the Lord of the place whither I go; and that, as you say, to cover my nakedness with. And I take it as a token of his kindness to me; for I had nothing but rags before. And besides, thus I comfort myself as I go: Surely, think I, when I come to the gate of the city, the Lord thereof will know me for good, since I have his coat on my back—a coat that he gave me freely in the day that he stripped me of my rags. I have, moreover, a mark in my forehead, which one of my Lord's most intimate associates fixed there in the day that my burden fell off my shoulders. I had then given me a roll, sealed, to comfort me by reading as I go on the way; I was also bid to give it in at the Celestial Gate, in token of my certain going in after it; all which things, I doubt, you want, and lack them because you came not in at the gate.

To these things they gave him no answer ; only they looked upon each other, and laughed. Then I saw that they went on all, save that Christian kept before, who had no more talk but with himself, sometimes sighingly and sometimes comfortably ; also he would be often reading in the roll that one of the Shining Ones gave him, by which he was refreshed.

I beheld, then, that they all went on till they came to the foot of the Hill Difficulty ; at the bottom of which was a spring. There were also in the same place two other ways besides that which came straight from the gate ; one turned to the left hand, and the other to the right, at the bottom of the hill ; but the narrow way lay right up the

HE STUMBLED AND FELL, AND ROSE NO MORE.

hill, and the name of the going up the side of the hill is called Difficulty. Christian now went to the spring, and drank thereof, to refresh himself, and then began to go up the hill.

The other two also came to the foot of the hill ; but when they saw that the hill was steep and high, and that there were two other ways to go; and supposing also that these two ways might meet again, with that up which Christian went, on the other side of the hill ; therefore they resolved to go in those ways. Now the name of one of those ways was Danger, and the name of the other Destruction. So the one took the way which is called Danger, which led him into a great wood, and the other took directly up the way to Destruction, which led him into a wide field, full of dark mountains, where he stumbled and fell, and rose no more.

I looked, then, after Christian, to see him go up the hill, where I perceived he fell from running to going, and from going to clambering upon his hands and his knees, because of the steepness of the place. Now, about the midway to the top of the hill was a pleasant arbor, made by the Lord of the hill for the refreshing of weary travellers; thither, therefore, Christian got, and sat down to rest. Then he pulled his roll out of his bosom, and read therein to his comfort; he now began afresh to take a review of the coat or garment that was given him as he stood by the cross. Thus pleasing himself a while, he at last fell into a slumber, and thence into a fast sleep, which detained him in that place until it was almost night; and in his sleep his roll fell out of his hand. Now, as he was sleeping, there came one to him, and awaked him, saying, "Go to the ant, thou sluggard; consider her ways, and be wise." And with that Christian started up, and sped him on his way, and went apace, till he came to the top of the hill.

Now, when he was got up to the top of the hill, there

came two men running to meet him amain ; the name of the one was Timorous, and of the other Mistrust ; to whom Christian said, Sirs, what's the matter ? You run the wrong way. Timo-rous answered, that they were going to the City of Zion, and had got up that difficult place ; but, said he, the further we go, the more danger we meet with ; where-fore we turned, and are going back again.

Yes, said Mistrust, for just before us lie a couple of lions in the way, whether sleeping or waking we know not, and we could not think, if we came within reach, but they would present-ly pull us in pieces.

CHRISTIAN. You make me afraid, but whither shall I fly to be safe ? If I go back to mine own country, *that* is prepared for fire and brimstone, and I shall certainly perish there. If I can get to the Celestial City, I am

HE AT LAST FELL INTO A SLUMBER.

sure to be in safety there. I must venture. To go back is nothing but death ; to go forward is fear of

death, and life everlasting beyond it. I will yet go
forward. So Mistrust and Timorous ran down the hill,
and Christian went on his way. But thinking again of
what he had heard from the men, he felt in his bosom
for his roll, that he might read therein, and be comforted ; but he felt, and found it not. Then was Christian in great distress, and knew not what to do; for he
wanted that which used to relieve him, and that which
should have been his pass into the Celestial City. Here,
therefore, he began to be much perplexed, and knew
not what to do. At last he bethought himself that he
had slept in the arbor that is on the side of the hill ;
and, falling down upon his knees, he asked God's forgiveness for that his foolish act, and then went back
to look for his roll. But all the way he went back,
who can sufficiently set forth the sorrow of Christian's
heart ! Sometimes he sighed, sometimes he wept, and
oftentimes he chid himself for being so foolish to fall
asleep in that place, which was erected only for a little
refreshment for his weariness. Thus, therefore, he
went back, carefully, looking on this side and on that,
all the way as he went, if happily he might find his roll,
that had been his comfort so many times in his journey.
He went thus, till he came again within sight of the
arbor where he sat and slept ; but that sight renewed
his sorrow the more by bringing again, even afresh,
his evil of sleeping into his mind. Thus, therefore, he
now went on bewailing his sinful sleep, saying, "O
wretched man that I am !" that I should sleep in the
daytime ! that I should sleep in the midst of difficulty !
that I should so indulge the flesh, as to use that rest for
ease to my flesh, which the Lord of the hill hath erected
only for the relief of the spirits of pilgrims !

How many steps have I took in vain ! Thus it hap-

MISTRUST.

pened to Israel, for their sin ; they were sent back again by the way of the Red Sea ; and I am made to tread those steps with sorrow, which I might have trod with delight, had it not been for this sinful sleep. How far might I have been on my way by this time ! I am made to tread those steps thrice over, which I needed not to have trod but once ; yea, now also I am like to be benighted, for the day is almost spent. Oh, that I had not slept !

Now, by this time he was come to the arbor again, where for a while he sat down and wept ; but at last, as Christian would have it, looking sorrowfully down under the settle, there he espied his roll ; which with trembling and haste he snatched up, and put it in his bosom. But who can tell how joyful this man was when he had gotten his roll again! for this roll was the assurance of his life and acceptance at the desired haven. Therefore he laid it up in his bosom, gave thanks to God for directing his eye to the place where it lay, and with joy and tears betook himself again to his journey. But oh, how nimbly now did he go up the rest of the hill ! Yet, before he got up the sun went down upon Christian ; and this made him again recall the vanity of his sleeping to his remembrance ; and thus he again began to condole with himself. O thou sinful sleep: how, for thy sake am I like to be benighted in my journey. I must walk without the sun ; darkness must cover the path of my feet ; and I must hear the noise of the doleful creatures, because of my sinful sleep. Now also he remembered the story that Mistrust and Timorous told him of, how they were frighted with the sight of the lions. Then said Christian to himself again, These beasts range in the night for their prey ; and if they should meet with me in the dark, how

TIMOROUS.

should I shift them? How should I escape being torn in pieces? Thus he went on his way. But while he was thus bewailing his unhappy miscarriage, he lift up his eyes, and behold there was a very stately palace before him, the name of which was Beautiful; and it stood just by the highway side.

So I saw in my dream that he made haste and went forward, that if possible he might get lodging there. Now, before he had gone far, he entered into a very narrow passage, which was about a furlong from the porter's lodge; and looking very narrowly before him as he went, he espied two lions in the way. Now, thought he, I see the dangers that Mistrust and Timorous were driven back by. (The lions were chained, but he saw not the chains.) Then he was afraid, and thought also himself to go back, for he feared nothing but death was before him. But the porter at the lodge, whose name is Watchful, perceiving that Christian made a halt as if he would go back, cried unto him, saying, Is thy strength so small? Fear not the lions, for they are chained, and are placed there for trial of faith where it is, and for discovery of those that had none. Keep in the midst of the path, and no hurt shall come unto thee.

Then he went on, trembling for fear of the lions, but taking good heed to the directions of the porter; he heard them roar, but they did him no harm. Then he clapped his hands, and went on till he came and stood before the gate where the porter was. Then said Christian to the porter, Sir, what house is this? And may I lodge here to-night? The porter answered, This house was built by the Lord of the hill, and he built it for the relief and security of pilgrims. The porter also asked whence he was, and whither he was going.

THE LIONS WERE CHAINED, BUT HE SAW NOT THE CHAINS

CHRISTIAN. I am come from the City of Destruction, and am going to Mount Zion ; but because the sun is now set, I desire, if I may, to lodge here to-night.

PORTER. What is your name ?

My name is now Christian, but my name at the first was Graceless ; I came of the race of Japheth, whom God will persuade to dwell in the tents of Shem.

PORTER. But how doth it happen that you come so late ? The sun is set.

CHRISTIAN. I had been here sooner, but "wretched man that I am !"—I slept in the arbor that stands on the hill-side ; I had, notwithstanding that, been here much sooner, but that, in my sleep, I lost my evidence, and came without it to the brow of the hill ; and then feeling for it, and finding it not, I was forced with sorrow of heart to go back to the place where I slept my sleep, where I found it, and now I am come.

PORTER. Well, I will call out one of the virgins of this place, who will, if she likes your talk, bring you in to the rest of the family, according to the rules of the house. So Watchful, the porter, rang a bell, at the sound of which came out at the door of the house a grave and beautiful damsel, named Discretion, and asked why she was called.

The porter answered, This man is on a journey from the City of Destruction to Mount Zion, but being weary and benighted, he asked me if he might lodge here to-night.

Then she asked him whence he was, and whither he was going ; and he told her. She asked him also how he got into the way ; and he told her. Then she asked him what he had seen and met with in the way ; and he told her. And last she asked his name ; so he said, It is Christian, and I have so much the more a desire to lodge here to-night, because by what I perceive, this place was built by the Lord of the hill, for the relief and security of pilgrims. So she smiled, but the water stood in her eyes; and after a little pause, she said, I will call forth two or three more of the family. So she ran to the door, and called out Prudence, Piety, and Charity, who, after a little more discourse with him, had him into the family; and many of them, meeting him at the threshold of the house, said, "Come in, thou blessed of the Lord;" this house was built by the Lord of the hill, on purpose to entertain such pilgrims in. Then he bowed his head, and followed them into the house. So when he was come in and set down, they gave him something to drink, and consented together, that until supper was ready, some of them should have some particular discourse with Christian, for the best improvement

WATCHFUL THE PORTER.

of time ; and they appointed Piety and Prudence and Charity to discourse with him; and thus they began :

PIETY. Come, good Christian, since we have been

so loving to you, to receive you in our house this night, let us talk with you of all things that have happened to you in your pilgrimage. What moved you at first to betake yourself to a pilgrim's life?

CHRISTIAN. I was driven out of my native country by a dreadful sound that was in mine ears; to wit, that unavoidable destruction did attend me, if I abode in that place where I was.

PIETY. But how did it happen that you came out of your country this way?

CHRISTIAN. It was as God would have it; for when I was under the fears of destruction, I did not know whither to go; but by chance there came a man, as I was trembling and weeping, whose name is Evangelist, and he directed me to the wicket-gate, which else I should never have found, and so set me into the way that hath led me directly to this house.

PIETY. But did you not come by the house of the Interpreter?

CHRISTIAN. Yes, and did see such things there, the remembrance of which will stick by me as long as I live. The Interpreter took me and showed me a stately palace, and how the people were clad in gold that were in it; and how there came a venturous man, and cut his way through the armed men that stood in the door to keep him out; and how he was bid to come in, and win eternal glory. Methought those things did ravish my heart! I would have stayed at that good man's house a twelvemonth, but that I knew I had further to go.

PIETY. Why, did you hear him tell his dream?

CHRISTIAN. Yes, and a dreadful one it was, I thought; it made my heart ache as he was telling of it; but yet I am glad I heard it.

PIETY.   Was that all you saw at the house of the Interpreter?   And what saw you else in the way?

CHRISTIAN.   Saw! why, I went but a little further, and I saw one, as I thought in my mind, hang bleeding upon the tree ; and the very sight of him made my burden fall off my back (for I groaned under a very heavy burden,) but then it fell down from off me.   Yea, and while I stood looking up, for then I could not forbear looking, three Shining Ones came to me.   One of them testified that my sins were forgiven me ; another stripped me of my rags, and gave me this broidered coat which you see ; and the third set the mark which you see in my forehead, and gave me this sealed roll. (And with that he plucked it out of his bosom.)

PIETY.   But you saw more than this, did you not?

CHRISTIAN.   Some other matters I saw, as, namely: three men, Simple, Sloth, and Presumption, lie asleep a little out of the way, as I came, with irons upon their heels ; but I could not awake them.   Formalist and Hypocrisy also tumbled over the wall, to go, as they pretended, to Zion, but were quickly lost, as I myself did tell them they would be.   I found it hard work to get up this hill, and as hard to come by the lions' mouths ; and truly if it had not been for the good man, the porter that stands at the gate, I do not know but that after all I might have gone back again ; but now, I thank God I am here, and I thank you for receiving me.

Then Prudence thought to ask him a few questions, and desired his answer to them.

PRUDENCE.   Do you not think sometimes of the country from whence you came?

CHRISTIAN.   Yes, but with much shame and detestation.

PRUDENCE. Do you not yet bear away with you some of the things that then you were conversant withal?

CHRISTIAN. Yes, but greatly against my will; especially my inward and carnal cogitations, with which all my countrymen, as well as myself, were delighted; but now all those things are my grief.

PRUDENCE. Do you not find sometimes, as if those things were vanquished, which at other times are your perplexity?

CHRISTIAN. Yes, but that is seldom; but they are to me golden hours in which such things happen to me.

PRUDENCE. Can you remember by what means you find your annoyances, at times, as if they were vanquished?

CHRISTIAN. Yes, when I think what I saw at the cross, that will do it; and when I look upon my broidered coat, that will do it; also when I look into the roll that I carry in my bosom, that will do it; and when my thoughts wax warm about whither I am going, that will do it.

PRUDENCE. And what is it that makes you so desirous to go to Mount Zion?

CHRISTIAN. Why, there I hope to see him alive that did hang dead on the cross; and there I hope to be rid of all those things that to this day are in me an annoyance to me; there, they say, there is no death; and there I shall dwell with such company as I like best. I would fain be where I shall die no more, and with the company that shall continually cry, "Holy, Holy, Holy!"

Then said Charity to Christian, Have you a family? Are you a married man?

CHRISTIAN. I have a wife and four small children.

CHARITY. And why did you not bring them along with you?

The Pilgrim's Progress—3.

"'I WILL SEARCH THEM IN THE MORNING.'"

See page 120.

CHRISTIAN. Then Christian wept, and said, Oh, how willingly would I have done it ! but they were all of them utterly averse to my going on pilgrimage.

CHARITY. But you should have talked to them, and endeavored to have shown them the danger of being behind.

CHRISTIAN. So I did; and told them also what God had shown to me of the destruction of our city ; "but I seemed to them as one that mocked," and they believed me not.

CHARITY. And did you pray to God that he would bless your counsel to them ?

CHRISTIAN. Yes, and that with such affection ; for you must think that my wife and poor children were very dear unto me.

CHARITY. But did you tell them of your own sorrow and fear of destruction ?

CHRISTIAN. Yes, over, and over, and over. They might also see my fears in my countenance, in my tears, and also in my trembling under the apprehension of the judgment that did hang over our heads ; but all was not sufficient to prevail with them to come with me. My wife was afraid of losing this world, and my children were given to the foolish delights of youth ; so what by one thing, and what by another, they left me to wander in this manner alone.

CHARITY. But did you not, with your vain life, damp all that you by words used by way of persuasion to bring them away with you ?

CHRISTIAN. Indeed, I can not commend my life ; for I am conscious to myself of many failings therein ; I know also, that a man by his conversation may soon overthrow, what by argument or persuasion he doth labor to fasten upon others for their good. Yet this I can say, I was very wary of giving them occasion, by any unseemly action, to make them averse to going on pilgrimage. Yea, for this very thing they would tell me I was too precise, and that I denied myself of things, for their sakes, in which they saw no evil. Nay, I think I may say that, if what they saw in me did hinder them, it was my great tenderness in sinning against God, or of doing any wrong to my neighbor.

Now I saw in my dream, that thus they sat talking together until supper was ready. So when they had made ready, they sat down to meat. Now the table was furnished "with fat things, and with wine that was well refined ; " and all their talk at the table was about the Lord of the hill ; about what he had done, wherefore he did what he did, and why he had builded that house. And by what they said, I perceived that he had been a great warrior, and had fought with and slain "him that had the power of death," but not without great danger to himself, which made me love him the more. For, as they said, he did it with the loss of much blood ; but that which put glory of grace into all he did, was, that he did it out of pure love to his country. And besides, there were some of them of the household that said they had been and spoke with him since he did die on the cross ; and they have attested that they had it from his own lips, that he is such a lover of poor pilgrims, that the like is not to be found from the east to the west.

They, moreover, gave an instance of what they affirmed, and that was, he had stripped himself of his glory, that he might do this for the poor ; and that they heard him say and affirm "that he would not dwell in the mountain of Zion alone." They said, moreover, that he had made many pilgrims princes, though by nature they were beggars born, and their original had been the dunghill.

Thus they discoursed together till late at night, and after they had committed themselves to their Lord for protection, they betook themselves to rest; the pilgrim they laid in a large upper chamber, whose window opened toward the sun-rising; the name of the chamber was Peace.

So in the morning after some more discourse, they told him that he should not depart till they had shown him the rarities of that place. And first they had him into the study, where they showed him records of the greatest antiquity ; in which, as I remember my dream, they showed him first the pedigree of the Lord of the hill, that he was the son of the Ancient of Days, and came by that eternal generation. Here also was more fully recorded the acts that he had done, and the names of many hundreds that he had taken into his service : and how he had placed them in such habitations, that could neither by length of days, nor decays of nature, be dissolved.

Then they read to him some of the worthy acts that some of his servants had done : as, how they had " subdued kingdoms, wrought righteousness, obtained promises, stopped the mouths of lions, quenched the violence of fire, escaped the edge of the sword, out of weakness were made strong, waxed valiant in fight, and turned to flight the armies of the aliens."

They then read again, in another part of the records of the house, where it was showed how willing their Lord was to receive into his favor any, even any though they in time past had offered great affronts to his person and proceedings.

The next day they took him into the armory, where

they showed him all manner of furniture, which their Lord had provided for pilgrims, as sword, shield, helmet, breastplate, *all-prayer*, and shoes that would not wear out. And there was here enough of this to harness out as many men for the service of their Lord as there be stars in the heaven for multitude.

They also showed him some of the engines with which some of his servants had done wonderful things. They showed him Moses' rod ; the hammer and nail with which Jael slew Sisera ; the pitchers, trumpets, and lamps too, with which Gideon put to flight the armies of Midian. Then they showed him the ox's goad wherewith Shamgar slew six hundred men. They showed him also the jaw-bone with which Samson did such mighty feats. They showed him, moreover, the sling and stone with which David slew Goliath of Gath ; and the sword, also, with which their Lord will kill the Man of Sin, in the day that he shall rise up to the prey. They showed him, besides, many excellent things, with which Christian was much delighted.

Then I saw in my dream, that on the morrow he got up to go forward ; but they desired him to stay till the next day also ; and then, said they, we will, if the day be clear, show you the Delectable Mountains, which, they said, would yet further add to his comfort, because they were nearer the desired haven than the place where at present he was ; so he consented and stayed. When the morning was up, they had him to the top of the house, and bid him look south ; so he did : and behold, at a great distance, he saw a most pleasant mountainous country, beautified with woods, vineyards, fruits of all sorts, flowers also, with springs and fountains, very delectable to behold. Then he asked the name of the country. They said it was Immanuel's Land ; and it is as free, said they, as this hill is, to and for all the pilgrims. From thence, said they, thou mayest see to the gate of the Celestial City.

Now he bethought himself of setting forward, and they were willing he should. But first, said they, let us go again into the armory. So they did ; and when they came there, they harnessed him from head to foot with what was of proof, lest, perhaps, he should meet with assaults on the way. He being, therefore, thus accoutred, walketh out with his friends to the gate and there he asked the porter if he saw any pilgrim pass by. Then the porter answered, Yes. I asked him his name, and he told me it was Faithful.

CHRISTIAN. Oh, said Christian, I know him ; he is my townsman, my near neighbor. How far do you think he may be before ?

PORTER. He is got by this time below the hill.

CHRISTIAN. Well, good Porter, the Lord be with thee, and add to all thy blessings much increase, for the kindness that thou hast showed to me.

Then he began to go forward ; but Discretion, Piety, Charity, and Prudence, would accompany him down to the foot of the hill. Then said Christian, As it was difficult coming up, so, so far as I can see, it is danger-ous going down. Yes, said Prudence, so it is, for it is a hard matter for a man to go down into the Valley of Humiliation, as thou art now, and to catch no slip by the way ; therefore, said they, are we come out to ac-company thee down the hill. So he began to go down but very warily ; yet he caught a slip or two.

Then I saw in my dream that these good companions, when Christian was gone to the bottom of the hill, gave him a loaf of bread, a bottle of wine, and a cluster of raisins ; and then he went on his way.

But now, in this Valley of Humiliation, poor Christian had gone but a little way, before he espied a foul fiend coming over the field to meet him ; his name was Apollyon. Then did Christian begin to be afraid, and undecided whether to go back or to stand his ground. But he considered again that he had no armor for his back ; and to turn the back to him might give him the greater advantage to pierce him with his darts ; so he resolved to stand his ground ; for, thought he, had I no more in mine eye than the saving of my life, it would be the best way to stand.

So he went on, and Apollyon met him. Now the monster was hideous to behold ; he was clothed with scales, like a fish, he had wings like a dragon, feet like a bear, and out of his belly came fire and smoke, and his mouth was as the mouth of a lion. When he was come up to Christian, he beheld him with a disdainful countenance, and thus began to question with him.

APOLLYON. Whence came you ? and whither are you bound ?

CHRISTIAN. I am come from the City of Destruction, which is the place of all evil, and am going to the City of Zion.

APOLLYON. By this I perceive that thou art one of my subjects, for all that country is mine, and I am the prince and god of it. How is it, then, thou hast run away from thy king ? Were it not that I hope thou mayest do me more service, I would strike thee now at one blow, to the ground.

CHRISTIAN. I was born, indeed, in your dominions, but your service was hard, and your wages such as a man could not live on, "for the wages of sin *is* death ;" therefore, when I was come to years, I did as other considerate persons do. look out if perhaps I might mend myself.

APOLLYON. There is no prince that will thus lightly lose his subjects, neither will I as yet lose thee ; but since thou complainest of thy service and wages, be content to go back ; what our country will afford, I do here promise to give thee.

CHRISTIAN. But I have let myself to another, even to the King of princes ; and how can I, with fairness, go back with thee ?

APOLLYON. Thou hast in this, "Changed a bad for a worse ;" but it is ordinary for those that have professed themselves his servants, after a while to give him the slip, and return again to me. Do thou so too, and all shall be well.

CHRISTIAN. I have given him my faith, and sworn my allegiance to him ; how, then, can I go back from this, and not be hanged as a traitor ?

APOLLYON. Thou didst the same to me, and yet I am willing to pass by all, if now thou wilt yet turn again and go back.

CHRISTIAN. What I promised thee was in my nonage ; and, besides, I count the Prince under whose banner now I stand is able to absolve me ; yea, and to pardon also what I did as to my compliance with thee ; and besides, O thou destroying Apollyon ! to speak truth, I like his service, his wages, his servants, his government, his company and country, better than thine ; and, therefore, leave off to persuade me further ; I am his servant and I will follow him.

APOLLYON. Consider, again, when thou art in cool blood, what thou art like to meet with in the way that thou goest. Thou knowest that, for the most part, his servants came to an ill end, because they are transgressors against me and my ways. How many of them have been put to shameful deaths ; and, besides, thou countest his service better than mine, whereas he never came yet from the place where he is to deliver any that served him out of their hands ; but as for me, how many times, as all the world very well knows, have I delivered, either by power, or fraud, those that have faithfully served me, from him and his, though taken by them ; and so I will deliver thee.

CHRISTIAN. His forebearing at present to deliver them is on purpose to try their love, whether they will cleave to him to the end ; and as for the ill end thou sayest they come to, that is most glorious in their account ; for, for present deliverance, they do not much expect it, for they stay for their glory, and then they shall have it, when their Prince comes in his and the glory of the angles.

APOLLYON. Thou hast already been unfaithful in thy service to him ; and how dust thou think to receive wages of him ?

CHRISTIAN. Wherein, O Apollyon, have I been unfaithful to him ?

APOLLYON. Thou didst faint at first setting out, when thou wast almost choked in the Gulf of Despond ; thou didst attempt wrong ways to get rid of thy burden, whereas thou shouldest have stayed till thy Prince had taken it of ; thou didst sinfully sleep and lose thy choice thing ; thou wast, also, almost persuaded to go back, at the sight of the lions ; and when thou talkest of thy journey, and of what thou hast heard and seen, thou art inwardly desirous of vainglory in all that thou sayest or doest.

CHRISTIAN. All this is true, and much more which thou hast left out! but the Prince whom I serve and honor is merciful, and ready to forgive ; but, besides, these infirmities possessed me in thy country, for there

I sucked them in ; and I have groaned under them, been sorry for them, and have obtained pardon of my Prince.

Then Apollyon broke out into a grievous rage, saying, I am an enemy to this Prince ; I hate his person, his laws, and people ; I am come out on purpose to withstand thee.

CHRISTIAN. Apollyon, beware what you do ; for I am in the king's highway, the way of holiness ; therefore take heed to yourself.

Then Apollyon straddled quite over the whole breadth of the way, and said, I am void of fear in this matter ; prepare thyself to die, for I swear by my infernal den, that thou shall go no further ; here will I spill thy soul.

And with that he threw a flaming dart at his breast ; but Christian had a shield in his hand, with which he caught it, and so prevented the danger of that.

Then did Christian draw, for he saw it was time to bestir him ; and Apollyon as fast made at him, throwing darts as thick as hail, by the which, notwithstanding all that Christian could do to avoid it, Apollyon wounded him in his head, his hand, and foot. This made Christian give a little back ; Apollyon, therefore, followed his work amain, and Christian again took courage, and resisted as manfully as he could. This sore combat lasted for above half a day, even till Christian was almost quite spent ; for you must know that Christian, by reason of his wounds, must needs grow weaker and weaker.

Then Apollyon, espying his opportunity, began to gather up close to Christian, and wrestling with him, gave him a dreadful fall ; and with that Christian's sword flew out of his hand. Then said Apollyon, I am sure of thee now. And with that he had almost pressed him to death, so that Christian began to despair of life: but as God would have it, while Apollyon was fetching of his last blow, thereby to make a full end of this good man, Christian nimbly stretched out his hand for his sword and caught it, saying, "Rejoice not against me, O mine enemy: when I fall I shall arise;" and with that gave him a deadly thrust, which made him give back; as one that had received his mortal wound. Christian perceiving that, made at him again, saying, "Nay, in all these things we are more than conquerors through him that loved us." And with that Apollyon spread forth his dragon's wings and sped him away, that Christian for a season, saw him no more.

In this combat no man can imagine, unless he had seen and heard as I did, what yelling and hideous roaring Apollyon made all the time of the fight—he spake like a dragon; and, on the other side, what sighs and groans burst from Christian's heart. I never saw him all the while give so much as one pleasant look, till he perceived he had wounded Apollyon with his two-edged sword; then indeed, he did smile, and look upward, but it was the dreadfullest sight that ever I saw.

So when the battle was over, Christian said, "I will here give thanks to him that delivered me out of the mouth of the lion, to him that did help me against Apollyon."

Then there came to him a hand, with some of the leaves of the tree of life, the which Christian took, and applied to the wounds that he had received in the battle, and was healed immediately. He also sat down in that place to eat bread, and to drink of the bottle that was given him a little before; so, being refreshed, he addressed himself to his journey, with his sword drawn in his hand ; for he said, I know not bu; some other enemy may be at hand. But he met with no other affront from Apollyon quite through this valley.

Now, at the end of this valley was another, called the Valley of the Shadow of Death, and Christian must needs go through it, because the way to the Celestial City lay through the midst of it. Now, this valley is a very solitary place, and Christian was worse put to it than in his fight with Apollyon ; as you shall see.

I saw then in my dream, that when Christian was got to the borders of the Shadow of Death, there met him two men, children of them that brought up an evil report of the good land, making haste to go back ; to whom Christian spake as follows : Whither are you going ?

TO HIM LET ME GIVE LASTING PRAISE.

MEN. Back ! back ! and we would have you to do so too, if either life or peace is prized by you.

CHRISTIAN. Why, what's the matter ?

MEN. Matter ! we were going that way as you are going, and went as far as we durst ; and indeed we were almost past coming back; for had we gone a little further we had not been here to bring the news to thee.

CHRISTIAN. But what have you met with?

MEN. Why, we were almost in the Valley of the Shadow of Death; but that, by good hap, we looked before us, and saw the danger before we came to it.

CHRISTIAN. But what have you seen?

MEN. Seen! Why, the valley itself, which is as dark as pitch; we also saw there the hobgoblins, satyrs, and dragons of the pit; we heard also in that Valley a continual howling and yelling, as of a people under unutterable misery, who there sat bound in affliction and irons; and over that Valley hangs the discouraging clouds of confusion. Death also doth always spread his wings over it.

Then, said Christian, I perceive that this is my way to the desired haven.

MEN. Be it thy way; we will not choose it for ours.

So they parted, and Christian went on his way, but still with his sword drawn in his hand, for fear lest he should be assaulted.

I saw then in my dream so far as this valley reached, there was on the right hand a very deep ditch, into which the blind have led the blind in all ages, and both have there miserably perished. Again, behold on the left hand, there was a very dangerous quag, into which, if even a good man falls, he can find no bottom for his foot to stand on. Into that quag king David once did fall, and had no doubt therein been smothered, had not HE that is able plucked him out.

The pathway was here also exceedingly narrow, and therefore good Christian was the more put to it; for when he sought, in the dark, to shun the ditch on the one hand, he was ready to tip over into the mire on the other; also when he sought to escape the mire, without great carefulness he would be ready to fall into the ditch. Thus he went on, and I heard him here sigh

A COMPANY OF FIENDS.

bitterly; for, besides the dangers mentioned above, the pathway was here so dark, that oftimes when he lift up his foot to set forward, he knew not where or upon what he should set it next.

About the midst of this valley, I perceived the mouth of hell to be near by the way-side. Now, thought Christian, what shall I do? And ever and anon the flame and smoke would come out in such abundance, with sparks and hideous noises, (things that cared not for Christian's sword, as did Apollyon before,) that he was forced to put up his sword, and betake himself to another weapon, called All-prayer. So he cried in my hearing, "O Lord, I beseech thee, deliver my soul!" Thus he went on a great while, yet still the flames would be reaching towards him. Also he heard doleful voices, and rushings to and fro, so that sometimes he thought he should be torn in pieces, or trodden down like mire in the streets. This frightful sight was seen and these dreadful noises were heard by him for several miles together; and coming to a place where he thought he heard a company of fiends coming forward to meet him, he stopped, and began to muse what he had best to do. Sometimes he had half a thought to go back; then again he thought he might be half way through the valley; he remembered also how he had already vanquished many a danger, and that the danger of going back might be much more than for to go forward; so he resolved to go on. Yet the fiends seemed to come nearer and nearer; but when they were almost at him, he cried out with a most vehement voice, "I will walk in the strength of the Lord God!" so they gave back and came no further.

One thing I would not let slip; I took notice that now poor Christian was so confounded, that he did not know his own voice; and thus I perceived it. Just when he was come over against the mouth of the burning pit, one of the wicked ones got behind him, and stepped up softly to him, and whisperingly suggested

THE WICKED ONES GOT BEHIND HIM, AND WHISPERINGLY SUGGESTED
MANY GRIEVOUS BLASPHEMIES TO HIM. [79]

many grievous blamphemies to him, which he verily thought had proceeded from his own mind. This put Christian more to it than anything that he met with before, even to think that he should now blaspheme him that he loved so much before ; yet if he could have helped it, he would not have done it ; but he had not the discretion either to stop his ears, or to know from whence these blasphemies came.

When Christian had travelled in this disconsolate condition some considerable time, he thought he heard the voice of a man, as going before him, saying, " Though I walk through the valley of the shadow of death, I will fear no evil, for thou *art* with me."

Then he was glad.

By-and-by the day broke ; then said Christian, He hath turned " the shadow of death into the morning."

Now morning being come, he looked back, not out of desire to return, but to see, by the light of the day, what hazards he had gone through in the dark. So he saw more perfectly the ditch that was on the one hand, and the quag that was on the other ; also how narrow the way was which led betwixt them both ; also now he saw the hobgoblins, and satyrs, and dragons of the pit, but all afar off—for after break of day, they came not nigh.

Christian was now much affected with his deliverance from all the dangers of his solitary way. About this time the sun was rising, and this was another mercy to Christian ; for though the first part of the Valley of the Shadow of Death was dangerous, yet this second part far more dangerous. From the place where he now stood, even to the end of the valley, the way was all along set so full of " snares, traps, gins, and nets here, and so full of pits, pitfalls, deep holes, and shelvings down there, that, had it now been dark, as it was when he came the first part of the way, had he had a thousand souls, they had in reason been cast away."

Now I saw in my dream, that at the end of this valley lay blood, bones, ashes, and mangled bodies of men, even of pilgrims that had gone this way formerly; and while I was musing what should be the reason, I espied a little before me a cave, where two giants, POPE and PAGAN, dwelt in old time; by whose power and tyranny the men whose bones, blood, ashes, etc., lay there, were cruelly put to death. But by this place Christian went without much danger, whereat I somewhat wondered; but I have learnt since that PAGAN had been dead many a day; and as for the other, though he be yet alive, he is, by reason of age, and also of the many shrewd brushes that he met with in his younger days, grown so crazy and stiff in his joints, that he can now do little more than sit in his cave's mouth, grinning at pilgrims as they go by, and biting his nails because he cannot come at them. But he held his peace, and set a good face on it, and so went by and catched no hurt. Then sang Christian:

> "O world of wonders! (I can see no less)
> That I should be preserved in that distress
> That I have met with here ! O blessed be
> That hand that from it hath deliver'd me !
> Dangers in darkness, devils, hell, and sin,
> Did compass me, while I this vale was in:
> Yea, snares and pits, and traps, and nets, did lie
> My path about, that worthless, silly I
> Might have been catch'd, entangled, and cast down;
> But since I live, let JESUS wear the crown."

Now, as Christian went on his way, he came to a little ascent, which was cast up on purpose that pilgrims might see before them. Up there, therefore,

Christian went, and looking forward, he saw Faithful before him, upon his journey. Then said Christian aloud, "Ho! ho! Soho! stay, and I will be your companion!" At that, Faithful looked behind him; to whom Christian cried again, "Stay, stay, till I come up to you." But Faithful answered; "No, I am upon my life, and the avenger of blood is behind me."

At this Christian was somewhat moved, and putting to all his strength, he quickly got up with Faithful, and did also overrun him; so the last was first. Then did Christian vain-gloriously smile, because he had gotten the start of his brother; but not taking good heed to his feet, he suddenly stumbled and fell, and could not rise again until Faithful came up to help him.

Then I saw in my dream they went very lovingly on together, and had sweet discourse of all things that had happened to them in their pilgrimage; and thus they discoursed:

CHRISTIAN. How long, dear friend, did you stay in the City of Destruction, before you set out after me on your pilgrimage?

FAITHFUL. Till I could stay no longer; for there was great talk presently after you had gone out, that our city would in a short time, with fire from heaven, be burned down to the ground. I heard some of your neighbors deridingly speak of you and your desperate journey, but I do still believe that the end of our city will be with fire and brimstone from above.

CHRISTIAN. Did they speak of neighbor Pliable!

FAITHFUL. Oh yes! Since he hath gone back he hath been greatly derided among all sorts of people. He is now seven times worse than if he had never gone out of the city. They say, hang him, he is a turncoat, he is not true to his profession. I think God has stirred up even his enemies to hiss at him, and make him a proverb because he hath forsaken the way. I met him once in the streets, but he leered away on the other side, as one ashamed of what he had done.

CHRISTIAN. Well, neighbor Faithful, let us leave him, and talk of things that more immediately concern ourselves. Tell me now what you have met with in the way as you came.

FAITHFUL. I escaped the Slough that I perceived you fell into, and got up to the gate without that danger; only I met with one whose name was Wanton, who had like to have done me a mischief.

CHRISTIAN. It was well you escaped her net; Joseph was hard put to it by her, and he escaped her as you did; but it had like to have cost him his life. But what did she do to you?

FAITHFUL. You cannot think, but that you know something, what a flattering tongue she had; she lay at me hard to turn aside with her, promising me all manner of content.

CHRISTIAN. Nay, she did not promise you the content of a good conscience.

FAITHFUL. You know what I mean.

CHRISTIAN. Thank God, you have escaped her: "The abhored of the Lord shall fall into her ditch." Did you meet with no other assault as you came?

FAITHFUL. When I came to the foot of the hill called Difficulty, I met with a very aged man, who asked me what I was, and whither bound. I told him that I am a pilgrim, going to the Celestial City. Then said the old man, Thou lookest like an honest fellow; wilt thou be content to dwell with me for the wages that I shall give thee? Then I asked him his name, and where he dwelt. He said his name was Adam the First, and that he dwelt in the town of Deceit. He told me, that his work was many delights; and his wages, that I should be his heir at last. I further asked him what house he kept, and what other servants he had. So he told me, that his house was maintained with all the dainties in the world; and that his servants were those of his own begetting. Then I asked if he had any children. He said that he had but three daughters: the Lust of the Flesh, the Lust of the Eyes, and the Pride of Life, and that I should marry them all if I would. Then I asked how long time he would have me live with him? And he told me, As long as he lived himself. At first, I found myself somewhat inclinable to go with the man, for I thought he spake very fair; but looking in his forehead, as I talked with him, I saw there written, "Put off the old man with his deeds."

CHRISTIAN. And how then?

FAITHFUL. Then it came burning hot into my mind, whatever he said, and however he flattered, when he got me home to his house he would sell me for a slave. So I bid him forbear to talk, for I would not come near the door of his house. Then he reviled me, and told me that he would send such a one after me, that should make my way bitter to my soul. So I turned to go away from him; but just as I turned myself to go, I felt him take hold of my flesh, and give me such a deadly twitch back, that I thought he had pulled part of me after himself. So I went on my way up the hill. Now when I had got about half way up, I looked behind, and saw one coming after me, swift as the wind, so he overtook me just about the place where the settle stands.

CHRISTIAN. Just there, said Christian, did I sit down to rest me; but being overcome with sleep, I there lost this roll out of my bosom.

FAITHFUL. But, good Brother, hear me out. So soon as the man overtook me, he was but a word and a blow, for down he knocked me, and laid me for dead. But when I was a little come to myself again, I asked him wherefore he served me so. He said, because of my secret inclining to Adam the First: and with that he struck me another deadly blow on the breast, and beat me down backward; so I lay at his foot as dead as before. So, when I came to myself again I cried him mercy; but he said, I know not how to show mercy; and with that knocked me down again. He had doubtless made an end of me, but that one came by, and bid him forbear.

CHRISTIAN. Who was that that bid him forbear?

FAITHFUL. I did not know him at first, but as he went by, I perceived the holes in his hands and in his side; then I concluded that he was our Lord. So I went up the hill.

DISCONTENT.

CHRISTIAN. That man that overtook you was Moses. He spareth none, neither knoweth he how to show mercy to those that transgress his law.

FAITHFUL.   I know it very well; it was not the first time that he has met with me.   It was he that came to me when I dwelt securely at home, and that told me he would burn my house over my head if I stayed there.

CHRISTIAN.   But did you not see the house that stood there on the top of the hill, on the side of which Moses met you?

FAITHFUL.   Yes, and the lions too, before I came at it; but for the lions, I think they were asleep, for it was about noon; and because I had so much of the day before me, I passed by the porter, and came down the hill.

CHRISTIAN.   He told me, indeed, that he saw you go by, but I wished you had called at the house, for they would have showed you so many rarities, that you would scarce have forgot them to the day of your death.   But pray tell me, Did you meet nobody in the Valley of Humility?

FAITHFUL. . Yes, I met with one Discontent who would willingly have persuaded me to go back again with him, as the valley was altogether without honor, and to go there was to disobey my friends, Pride, Arrogancy, Self-conceit, Worldly-glory, with others, who, he knew, would be very much offended, if I made such a fool of myself as to wade through this valley.

CHRISTIAN.   Well, and how did you answer him.

FAITHFUL.   I told him that although all these might claim kindred of me, for indeed they were my relations according to the flesh; yet since I became a pilgrim, they have disowned me, as I also have rejected them; and now were no more than if they had never been of my lineage.   I also met with Shame; but of all the men that I met with in my pilgrimage, he, I think, bears

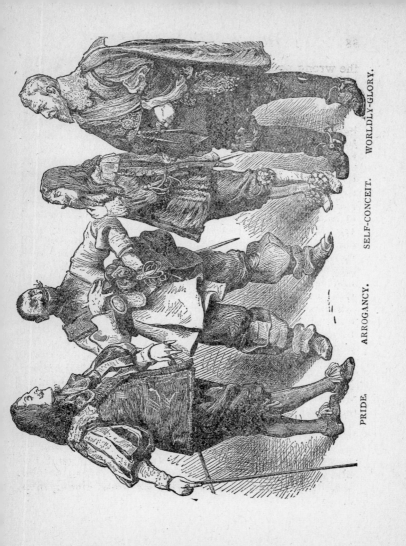

PRIDE. ARROGANCY. SELF-CONCEIT. WORLDLY-GLORY.

the wrong name. The others would be said nay, after a little argumentation, and somewhat else; but this bold-faced Shame would never have done.

CHRISTIAN. Why, what did he say to you?

FAITHFUL. What! why, he objected against religion itself; he said it was a pitiful, low, sneaking business, for a man to mind religion; he said that a tender conscience was an unmanly thing; and that for a man to watch over his words and ways, so as to tie up himself from that hectoring liberty that the brave spirits of the times accustom themselves unto, would make him the ridicule of the times. He objected also, that but few of the mighty, rich, or wise, were ever of my opinion. He, moreover, objected the base and low estate and condition of those that were chiefly the pilgrims of the times in which they lived, also their ignorance and want of understanding in all natural science. Yea, he did hold me to it at that rate also, about a great many more things than here I relate; as, that it was a *shame* to sit whining and mourning under a sermon, and a *shame* to come sighing and groaning home; that it was a *shame* to ask my neighbor forgiveness for petty faults, or to make restitution where I have taken from any. He said, also, that religion made a man grow strange to the great, because of a few vices, which he called by finer names; and made him own and respect the base because of the same religious fraternity. And is not this said he, a *shame?*

CHRISTIAN. And what did you say to him?

FAITHFUL. Say! I could not tell what to say at the first. Yea, he put me so to it, that my blood came up in my face; even this Shame fetched it up, and had almost beat me quite off. But at last I began to consider that "that which is highly esteemed among men, is had in abomination with God." And I thought again, this Shame tells me what men are, but it tells me nothing what God or the Word of God is. And I thought, moreover, that at the day of doom, we shall not be doomed to death or life according to the hectoring spirits of the world, but according to the wisdom and law of the Highest. Therefore, thought I, what God says is best, indeed is best, though all the men in the world are against it. Seeing, then, that God prefers his religion; seeing God prefers a tender conscience; seeing they that make themselves fools for the kingdom of heaven are wisest; and that the poor man that loveth Christ is richer than the greatest man in the world that hates him; *Shame*, depart, thou art an enemy to my salvation! Shall I entertain thee against my sovereign Lord? How then shall I look him in the face at his coming? Shame was a bold villain. He would be haunting me, and continually whispering to me some one or other of the infirmities that attend religion; but at last I told him it was but in vain to attempt further in this business; so I got past this importunate one.

CHRISTIAN. It was well for you. I am sure it fared far otherwise with me; I had for a long season, as soon almost as I entered into that valley, a dreadful combat with that foul fiend Apollyon; yea, I thought verily he would have killed me; especially when he got me down and crushed me under him, as if he would have crushed me to pieces; for as he threw me, my sword flew out of my hand; nay, he told me he was sure of me: but I cried to God, and he heard me, and delivered me out of all my troubles.

Moreover, I saw in my dream, that as they went on, Faithful, as he chanced to look on one side, saw a man whose name is Talkative, walking at a distance beside them; for in this place there was room enough for them all to walk. He was a tall man, and something more comely at a distance than at hand. To this man Faithful addressed himself in this manner.

FAITHFUL. Friend, whither away? Are you going to the heavenly country?

TALKATIVE. I am going to the same place.

FAITHFUL. That is well; then I hope we may have your good company.

TALKATIVE. With a very good will will I be your companion. To talk of things that are good, to me is very acceptable, with you or with any other; and I am glad that I have met with those that incline to so good a work; for, to speak the truth, there are but few that care thus to spend their time as they are in their travels, but choose much rather to be speaking of things to no profit.

FAITHFUL. That is indeed a thing to be lamented.

TALKATIVE. I like you wonderful well, for your sayings are full of conviction; and I will add, what thing is so pleasant, and what so profitable, as to talk of the things of God? For instance, if a man doth delight to talk of the history or the mystery of things; or if a man doth love to talk of miracles, wonders, or signs, where shall he find things recorded so delightful, and so sweetly penned, as in the Holy Scripture?

FAITHFUL. Well, then, what is that one thing that we shall at this time found our discourse upon?

TALKATIVE. What you will. I will talk of things heavenly, or things earthly; things moral, or things evangelical; things sacred, or things profane; things past, or things to come; things foreign, or things at home; things more essential, or things circumstantial: provided that all be done to our profit.

Faithful began to wonder; and stepping to Christian, he said to him softly, What a brave companion have we got! Surely this man will make a very excellent pilgrim.

Christian modestly smiled, and said, This man, with whom you are so taken, will beguile with that tongue of his, twenty of them that know him not.

Faithful. Do you know him then?

Christian. Know him! Yes, better than he knows himself.

Faithful. Pray, what is he?

Christian. His name is Talkative; he dwelleth in our town. I wonder that you should be a stranger to him. He is the son of one Say-well, and is known of all that are acquainted with him by the name of Talkative in Prating Row.

Faithful. Well, he seems to be a very pretty man?

Christian. That is to them who have not thorough acquaintance with him; for he is best abroad; near home, he is ugly enough.

Faithful. But I am ready to think that you but do jest, because you smiled.

Christian. God forbid that I should jest in this matter, or that I should accuse any falsely! I will tell you further of him. This man is for any company, and for any talk; as he talketh now with you, so will he talk on the ale-bench; and the more drink he hath in his crown the more of these things he hath in his mouth; religion hath no place in his heart, or house, or conversation; all he hath, lieth in his tongue, and his religion is to make a noise therewith.

Faithful. Say you so! then am I in this man greatly deceived.

Christian. Deceived! you may be sure of it; remember the proverb, "They say and do not." But the "kingdom of God is not in word, but in power." He talketh of prayer, of repentance, of faith, and of the new birth; but he knows but only to talk of them. His house is as empty of religion as the white of an egg is of savor. There is neither prayer, nor sign of repentance of sin there; yea, the brute in his kind serves God far better than he. He is the very stain, reproach, and shame of religion, to all who know him. Thus say the common people that know him, A saint abroad, and a devil at home. His poor family finds it so; he is such a churl, such a railer at, and so unreasonable with his servants, that they neither know how to do for or speak to him. This Talkative will defraud and beguil. Besides, he brings up his sons to follow his steps. I am of the opinion that he has, by his wicked life, caused many to stumble and fall; and will be, if God prevent not, the ruin of many more.

FAITHFUL. Well, I was not so fond of his company at first, but I am as sick of it now. What shall we do to be rid of him?

CHRISTIAN. Take my advice, and do as I bid you, and you shall find that he will soon be sick of your company too, except God shall touch his heart and turn it.

FAITHFUL. What would you have me do?

CHRISTIAN. Why, go to him, and enter into some serious discourse about the power of religion; and ask him plainly whether this thing be set up in his heart, house, or conversation.

FAITHFUL stepping forward again, said to Talkative, Come, what cheer? How is it now?

TALKATIVE. Thank you, well. I thought we should have had a great deal of talk by this time.

FAITHFUL. Well, if you will, we will fall to it now; and since you leave it to me, I will tell you all the truth. I have heard that you are a man whose religion lies in talk, and that your conversation gives this your mouth-profession the lie. They say, you are a spot among Christians; and that religion fareth the worse for your ungodly conversation; that some have already stumbled at your wicked ways, and that more are in danger of being destroyed thereby; your religion, and an ale-house, and covetousness, and uncleanness, and swearing, and lying, and vain-company keeping, etc., will stand together. You are a shame to all professors.

TALKATIVE. Since you are ready to take up reports and to judge so rashly as you do, I cannot but conclude you are some peevish or melancholy man, not fit to be discoursed with; and so adieu.

CHRISTIAN then came up, and said to his brother, I told you how it would happen; your words and his lusts could not agree: he had rather leave your company than reform his life. But he is gone, as I said; let him go, the loss is no man's but his own; he has saved us the trouble of going from him. You did well to talk so plainly to him as you did; there is but little of this faithful dealing with men nowadays, who make religion stink in the nostrils of many, as it doth; for they are these talkative fools whose religion is only in word, and who are debauched and vain in their conversation. I wish that all men would deal with such as you have done; then should they either be made more conformable to religion, or the company of saints would be too hot for them.

Thus they went on talking of what they had seen by the way, and so made that way easy which would otherwise, no doubt, have been tedious to them; for now they went through a wilderness.

Now, when they were got almost quite out of this wilderness, Faithful chanced to cast his eye back, and espied one coming after them, and he knew him. Oh! said Faithful to his brother, Who comes yonder? Then Christian looked and said, It is my good friend Evangelist. Ay, and my good friend too, said Faithful, for it was he that set me the way to the gate. Now was Evangelist come up to them, and thus saluted them:

EVANGELIST. Peace be with you, dearly beloved; and peace be to your helpers.

Then Christian and Faithful told him of all things that had happened to them in the way; and how, and with what difficulty, they had arrived to that place. Right glad am I, said Evangelist, not that you have met with trials, but that you have been victors; and for that you have, notwithstanding many weaknesses, continued in the way to this very day. I say, right glad am I of this thing, and that for mine own sake and yours. I have sowed, and you have reaped; and the day is coming, when both he that sowed and they that reaped shall rejoice together; that is, if you hold out: "for in due season ye shall reap, if ye faint not." The crown is before you, and it is an incorruptible one; "so run that you may obtain it." Some there be that set out for this crown, and, after they have gone far for it, another comes in, and takes it from them; hold fast, therefore, that you have; let no man take your crown. You are not yet out of the gun-shot of the devil; you have not resisted unto blood, striving against sin; let the kingdom be always before you, and believe steadfastly concerning things that are invisible. Let nothing that is on this side the other world get within you; and above all, look well to your own hearts and to the lusts thereof, "for they are deceitful above all things, and desperately wicked;" set your faces like a flint; you have all power in heaven and earth on your side.

Then Christian thanked him for his exhortation.

Then I saw in my dream, that when they were got out of the wilderness, they saw a town before them, and the name of that town is Vanity; and at the town there is a fair kept, called Vanity Fair; it is kept all the year long; it is so called, because the town where it is kept is lighter than vanity; and also because all that is there sold, or that cometh thither, is vanity. As is the saying of the wise, "all that cometh *is* vanity."

This fair is no new-erected business, but a thing of ancient standing; I will show you the original of it. Almost five thousand years agone, there were pilgrims walking to the Celestial City, as these two honest persons are; and Beelzebub, Apollyon, and Legion, with their companions, perceiving by the path that the pilgrims made, that their way to the city lay through this town of Vanity, they contrived here to set up a fair; a fair wherein should be sold all sorts of vanity, and that it should last all the year long; therefore at this fair are all such merchandise sold, as houses, lands, trades, places, honors, preferments, titles, countries, kingdoms, lusts, pleasures, and delights of all sorts.

And at all times is to be seen juggling, cheats, games, plays, fools, apes, knaves, and rogues, and that of every kind.

Here are to be seen, too, and that for nothing, thefts, murders, adulteries, false swearers, and that of a blood-red color.

And as in other fairs of less moment, there are several rows and streets, under their proper names, where such and such wares are vended; so here likewise you have the proper places, rows, streets, (viz., countries and kingdoms,) where the wares of this fair are soonest to be found. Here is the Britain Row, the French Row, the Italian Row, the Spanish Row, the German Row, where several sorts of vanities are to be sold. But, as in other fairs, some one commodity is as the chief of all the fair, so the ware of Rome and her merchandise is greatly promoted in this fair; only our English nation, with some others, have taken a dislike thereat.

Now, as I said, the way to the Celestial City lies just through this town where this lusty fair is kept; and he that will go to the City, and yet not go through this town, must needs "go out of the world." The Prince of princes himself, when here, went through this town to his own country, and that upon a fair day too; yea, and as I said, it was Beelzebub, the chief lord of this fair, that invited him to buy of his vanities; yea, would have made him lord of the fair, would he but have done him reverence as he went through the town. Yea, because he was such a person of honor, Beelzebub had him from street to street, and showed him all the kingdoms of the world in a little time, that he might, if possible, allure the Blessed One to cheapen and buy some of his vanities; but he had no mind to the merchandise, and therefore left the town without laying out so much as one farthing upon these vanities. This fair, therefore, is an ancient thing of long standing, and a very great fair. Now these pilgrims, as I said, must needs go through this fair. Well, so they did; but behold, even as they entered into the fair, all the people in the fair were moved, and the town itself as it were in a hubbub about them; and that for several reasons; for,

The pilgrims were clothed with such kind of raiment as was diverse from the raiment of any that traded in that fair. The people, therefore, of the fair, made a great gazing upon them; some said they were fools, some they were bedlams, and some they were outlandish men.

And as they wondered at their apparel, so they did likewise at their speech: for few could understand what they said; they naturally spoke the language of Canaan, but they that kept the fair were the men of this world; so that, from one end of the fair to the other they seemed barbarians each to the other.

But that which did not a little amuse the merchandisers was, that these pilgrims set very light by all their wares; they cared not so much as to look upon them, and if they called upon them to buy, they would put their fingers in their ears and cry, "Turn away mine eyes from beholding vanity," and look upwards, signifying that their trade and traffic was in heaven.

One chanced mockingly, beholding the carriage of the men, to say unto them, What will ye buy? But they, looking upon him, answered, "We buy the truth." At that there was an occasion taken to despise the men the more; some mocking, some taunting, some speaking reproachfully, and some calling upon others to smite them. At last things came to a hubbub and a great stir in the fair, insomuch that all order was confounded. Now was word presently brought to the great one of the fair, who quickly came down and deputed some of his most trusty friends to take these men into examination, about whom the fair was almost overturned. So the men were brought to examination; and they that sat upon them, asked them whence they came, whither they went, and what they did there, in such an unusual garb. The men told them that they were pilgrims and strangers in the world, and that they were going to their own country, which was the heavenly Jerusalem, and that they had given no occasion to the men of the town, nor yet to the merchandisers, thus to abuse them, except it was for that, when one asked them what they would buy, they said they would buy the truth. But they that were appointed to examine them did not believe them to be any other than bedlams and mad. Therefore they took them and beat them, and besmeared them with dirt, and put them into the cage, that they might be made a spectacle to all the men of the fair.

There, therefore, they lay for some time, and were made the objects of any man's sport, or malice, or revenge, the great one of the fair laughing still at all that befell them. But the men being patient, and not rendering railing for railing, but contrariwise, blessing, and giving good words for bad, and kindness for injuries done, some men in the fair that were more observing, and less prejudiced than the rest, began to check and blame the baser sort for their continual abuses to the men. They said that for aught they could see, the men were quiet, and sober, and intented nobody any harm; and that there were many that traded in their fair that were more worthy to be put into the cage, yea, and pillory too, than were the men they had abused.

After words had passed on both sides, the men behaving themselves all the while very wisely and soberly, they fell to blows among themselves. Then were these two poor men brought before their examiners again, and there charged as being guilty of the hubbub. So they beat them pitifully, and hanged irons upon them, and led them in chains up and down the fair, for an example and a terror to others, lest any should speak in

LORD HATE-GOOD.

their behalf, or join themselves unto them.   But Christian and Faithful behaved themselves with so much meekness and patience, that it won to their side, though but few in comparison of the rest, several of the men in the fair.   This put the other party yet into greater rage, insomuch that they concluded the death of these two men. Wherefore they threatened, that the cage nor irons should serve their turn, but that they should die, for the abuse they had done, and for deluding the men of the fair.   Then were they remanded to the cage again, until further order should be taken with them. So they put them in and made their feet fast in the stocks.

Then a convenient time being appointed, they brought them forth to their trial, in order to their condemnation. When the time was come, they were brought before their enemies and arraigned. The judge's name was Lord Hate-good. Their indictment was one and the same in substance, though somewhat varying in form, the contents whereof were this:

"That they were enemies to and disturbers of their trade; that they had made commotions and divisions in the town, and had won a party to their own most dangerous opinions, in contempt of the law of their prince."

Then Faithful began to answer, that he had only set himself against that which hath set itself against him that is higher than the highest. And, said he, as for disturbance, I make none, being myself a man of peace; the parties that were won to us, were won by beholding our truth and innocence, and they are only turned from the worse to the better. And as to the king you talk of, since he is Beelzebub, the enemy of our Lord, I defy him and all his angels.

Then proclamation was made, that they that had aught to say for their lord the king against the prisoner at the bar, should forthwith appear and give in their evidence. So there came in three witnesses, to wit, Envy, Superstition, and Pickthank. They were then asked if they knew the prisoner at the bar, and what they had to say for their lord the king against him.

Then stood forth Envy and Superstition who gave evidence against the prisoner.

Then was Pickthank sworn, and bid say what he knew, in behalf of their lord the king, against the prisoner at the bar.

PICKTHANK. My Lord, and you gentlemen all, this fellow I have known of a long time, and have heard him speak things that ought not to be spoke; for he hath railed on our noble prince Beelzebub, and hath spoken contemptibly of his honorable

ENVY.

friends, whose names are the Lord Old Man, the Lord Carnal Delight, the Lord Luxurious, the Lord Desire of Vain-Glory, my old Lord Lechery, Sir Having Greedy, with all the rest of our nobility; and he hath said, moreover, that if all men were of his mind, if possible, there is not one of these noblemen should have any longer a being in this town. Besides, he hath not been afraid to rail on you, my Lord, who

SUPERSTITION.

are now appointed to be his judge, calling you an ungodly villain, with many other such like vilifying terms, with which he hath bespattered most of the gentry of our town

When this Pickthank had told his tale, the Judge directed his speech to the prisoner at the bar, saying, Thou runagate, heretic, and traitor, hast thou heard what these honest gentlemen have witnessed against thee?

FAITHFUL. May I speak a few words in my own defence?

JUDGE. Sirrah! Sirrah! thou deservest to live no longer, but to be slain immediately upon the place; yet, that all men may see our gentleness towards thee, let us hear what thou, vile runagate, hast to say.

FAITHFUL. Then, in answer to what Mr. Envy hath spoken, I never said aught but this, That whatsoever is flat against the Word of God, is diametrically opposite to Christianity. If I have said amiss in this, convince me of my error, and I am ready here before you to make my recantation. As to Mr. Superstition, and his charge against me, I said only this, That in the worship of God there is required a Divine faith; but there can be no Divine faith without a Divine revelation of the will of God. As to what Mr. Pickthank hath said, I say that the prince of this town, with all the rabblement, his attendants, by this gentleman named, are more fit for being in hell than in this town and country; and so, the Lord have mercy upon me!

PICKTHANK.

Then the Judge called to the jury (who all this while stood by, to hear and observe): Gentlemen of the jury, you see this man about whom so great an uproar hath been made in this town. You have also heard what these worthy gentlemen have witnessed against him. Also you have heard his reply and confession. It lieth now in your breasts to hang him or save his life. You see he disputeth against our religion; and for the treason he hath confessed, he deserveth to die the death.

Then went the jury out, whose names were, Mr. Blind-man, Mr. No-good, Mr. Malice, Mr. Love-lust, Mr. Live-loose, Mr. Heady, Mr. High-mind, Mr. Enmity, Mr. Liar, Mr. Cruelty, Mr. Hate-light, and Mr. Implacable; who every one gave in his private verdict against him among themselves, and afterwards unanimously concluded to bring him in guilty before the Judge. And first, among themselves, Mr. Blind-man, the foreman, said, I see clearly that this man is a heretic. Then said Mr. No-good, Away with such a fellow from the earth. Ay, said Mr. Malice, for I hate the very looks of him. Then said Mr. Love-lust, I could never endure him. Nor I, said Mr. Live-loose, for he would always be condemning my way. Hang him, hang him, said Mr. Heady. A sorry scrub, said Mr. High-mind. My heart riseth against him, said Mr. Enmity. He is a rogue, said Mr. Liar. Hanging is too good for him, said Mr. Cruelty. Let us despatch him out of the way, said Mr. Hate-light. Then said Mr. Implacable, Might I have all the world given me, I could not be reconciled to him; therefore, let us forthwith bring him in guilty of death. And so they did; therefore he was presently condemned to be had from the place where he was, to the place from whence he came, and there to be put to the most cruel death that could be invented.

They, therefore, brought him out first, they scourged him, then they buffeted him, then they lanced his flesh with knives; after that, they stoned him with stones, then pricked him with their swords; and, last of all they burned him to ashes at the stake. Thus came Faithful to his end.

Now I saw that there stood behind the multitude a chariot and a couple of horses, waiting for Faithful,

THE JURY.

who (so soon as his adversaries had despatched him) was taken up into it; and straightway was carried up through the clouds, with sound of trumpet, the nearest way to the celestial gate.

But Christian had some respite, and was remanded back to prison. So he there remained for a space; but he that overrules all things, having the power of their rage in his own hand, so wrought it about, that Christian for that time escaped them, and went his way.

Now I saw in my dream, that Christian went not forth alone, for there was one whose name was Hopeful (being made so by the beholding of Christian and Faithful in their words and behavior, in their sufferings at the fair), who joined himself unto him, and, entering into a brotherly covenant, told him that he would be his companion. Thus, one died to bear testimony to the truth, and another rises out of his ashes, to be a companion with Christian in his pilgrimage. This Hopeful also told Christian, that there were many more of the men in the fair, that would take their time and follow after.

So I saw that quickly after they were got out of the fair, they overtook one that was going before them, whose name was By-ends: so they said to him, What countryman, Sir? and how far go you this way? He told them that he came from the town of Fair-speech, and he was going to the Celestial City, but told them not his name.

CHRISTIAN. From Fair-speech! Is there any good that lives there?

BY-ENDS. Yes, I hope.

CHRISTIAN. Pray, Sir, what may I call you?

BY-ENDS. I am a stranger to you, and you to me

if you be going this way, I shall be glad of your company; if not, I must be content.

CHRISTIAN. This town of Fair-speech, I have heard of; and, they say, it is a wealthy place.

BY-ENDS. Yes, I will assure you that it is; and I have very many rich kindred there.

CHRISTIAN. Pray, who are your kindred there? if a man may be so bold.

BY-ENDS. Almost the whole town; and in particular, my Lord Turn-about, my Lord Time-server, my Lord Fair-speech (from whose ancestors that town first took its name), also Mr. Smooth-man, Mr. Facing-both-ways, Mr. Anything; and the parson of our parish, Mr. Two-tongues, was my mother's own brother by father's side; and to tell you the truth, I am become a gentleman of good quality, yet my great-grandfather was but a waterman, looking one way and

BURNED TO ASHES AT THE STAKE.

rowing another, and I got most of my estate by the same occupation.

CHRISTIAN.   Are you a married man.

BY-ENDS.   Yes, and my wife is a virtuous woman, the daughter of a virtuous woman; she was my Lady Feigning's daughter, therefore she came of a very honorable family, and is arrived to such a pitch of breeding, that she knows how to carry it to all, even to prince and peasant.   It is true we somewhat differ in religion from those of the stricter sort, yet but in two small points: first, we never strive against wind and tide; secondly, we are always most zealous when religion goes in his silver slippers; we love much to walk with him in the streets, if the sun shines, and the people applaud him.

Then Christian stepped a little aside to his fellow, Hopeful, saying, It runs in my mind that this is one By-ends of Fair-speech; and if it be he, we have as very a knave in our company as dwelleth in all these parts.   So Christian came up with him again, and said, Sir, you talk as if you knew something more than all the world doth; is not your name Mr. By-ends of Fair-speech?

BY-ENDS.   This is not my name, but indeed it is a nickname that is given me by some that cannot abide me; and I must be content to bear it as a reproach, as other good men have borne theirs before me.

CHRISTIAN.   But did you never give an occasion to men to call you by this name?

BY-ENDS.   Never, never! The worst that ever I did to give them an occasion to give me this name was, that I had always the luck to jump in my judgment with the present way of the times, whatever it was, and my chance was to get thereby; but if things are thus cast upon me, let me count them a blessing; but let not the malicious load me therefore with reproach.

CHRISTIAN. If you will go with us, you must go against wind and tide; the which, I perceive, is against your opinion; you must also own Religion in his rags, as well as when in his silver slippers; and stand by him, too, when bound in irons, as well as when he walketh the streets with applause.

Then said By-ends, I shall never desert my old principles, since they are harmless and profitable.

Now I saw in my dream, that Christian and Hopeful forsook him, and kept their distance before him; but one of them looking back, saw three men following by Mr. By-ends, and behold, as they came up with him, he made them a very low *congé*; and they also gave him a compliment. The men's names were Mr. Hold-the-world, Mr. Money-love, and Mr. Save-all; men that Mr. By-ends had formerly been acquainted with; for in their minority they were school-fellows, and were taught by one Mr. Gripe-man, a schoolmaster in Love-gain, which is a market town in the county of Coveting, in the north. This schoolmaster taught them the art of getting, either by violence, cozenage, flattery, lying, or by putting on a guise of religion.

Well, when they had, as I said, thus saluted each other, Mr. Money-love said to Mr. By-ends, Who are they upon the road before us? (for Christian and Hopeful were yet within view.)

BY-ENDS. They are a couple of far countrymen, that, after their mode, are going on pilgrimage.

MONEY-LOVE. Alas! Why did they not stay, that we might have their good company?

BY-ENDS. We are so, indeed; but the men before us are so rigid, and love so much of their own notions, that if a man jumps not with them in all things, they thrust him out of their company.

Save-all.   That is bad, but we read of some that are righteous overmuch; rigidness prevails with them to judge and condemn all but themselves.

By-ends.   They, after their headstrong manner, conclude that it is duty to rush on their journey all weathers; and I am for waiting for wind and tide.   They are for Religion when in rags and contempt; but I am for him when he walks in his golden slippers, in the sunshine, and with applause.

Mr. Hold-the-world.   Ay, and hold you there still, good Mr. By-ends; for, for my part, I can count him but a fool, that, having the liberty to keep what he has, shall be so unwise as to lose it.

Mr. Save-all.   I think that we are all agreed in this matter, and therefore there needs no more words about it.

Christian and Hopeful the while went on till they came at a delicate plain called Ease, where they went with much content; but that plain was but narrow, so they quickly got over it.   Now at the further side of that plain was a hill called Lucre, and in that hill a silver mine, which some of them that had formerly gone that way, because of the rarity of it, had turned aside to see; but going too near the brink of the pit, the ground being deceitful under them, broke, and they were slain; some also had been maimed there, and could not, to their dying day, be themselves again.

Then I saw in my dream, that a little off the road, over against the silver mine, stood Demas (gentleman-like) to call to passengers to come and see; who said to Christian and his fellow, Ho! turn aside hither, and I will show you a thing.

CHRISTIAN. What thing so deserving as to turn us out of the way to see it?

DEMAS. Here is a silver mine, and some digging in it for treasure. If you will come, you may richly provide for yourselves.

HOPEFUL then said, Let us go see.

CHRISTIAN. No! I have heard of this place before now; and how many have there been slain; and besides that, treasure is a snare to those that seek it; for it hindereth them in their pilgrimage.

DEMAS. Not very dangerous, except to those that are careless, but he blushed as he spake.

CHRISTIAN then said to Hopeful, Let us not stir a step, but still keep on our way.

HOPEFUL. I will warrant you, when By-ends comes up, if he hath the same invitation as we, he will turn in to see.

CHRISTIAN. No doubt, for his principles lead him that way, and a hundred to one but he dies there.

Demas called again, saying, But will you not come over and see? Then Christian roundly answered, saying, Demas, thou art an enemy to the right ways of the Lord of this way, and hast been already condemned for thine own turning aside, by one of his Majesty's judges. Demas cried again, that he also was one of their fraternity; and that if they would tarry a little, he also himself would walk with them.

CHRISTIAN then said, What is thy name? Is it not the same by the which I have called thee?

DEMAS. Yes, my name is Demas; I am the son of Abraham.

CHRISTIAN. I know you; Gehazi was your great-grandfather, and Judas your father; and you have trod in their steps. Thy father was hanged for a traitor, and thou deservest no better reward.

Thus they went their way. By this time By-ends and his companions were come again within sight, and they, at the first beck, went over to Demas. Now, whether they fell into the pit or whether they went down to dig, or whether they were smothered by the damps that commonly arise, I am not certain; but I observed, that they never were seen again.

Just on the other side of this plain, the pilgrims came to a place where stood an old monument, at the sight of which they were both concerned, it seemed to them as if it had been a woman transformed into the shape of a pillar. At last Hopeful espied, written above the head thereof, a writing in an unusual hand. Christian, after a little laying of letters together, found the same to be this, "Remember Lot's wife." So he read it to his fellow; after which they both concluded that that was the pillar of salt into which Lot's wife was turned, for her looking back with a covetous heart, when she was going from Sodom for safety.

I saw, then, that they went on their way to a pleasant river; which David the king called "the river of God," but John, "the river of the water of life." Now their way lay just upon the bank of the river; here, therefore, Christian and his companion walked with great delight; they drank also of the water of the river, which was pleasant and enlivening to their weary spirits; besides, on the banks of this river, on either side, were green trees, that bore all manner of fruit, and the leaves of the trees were good for medicine; with the fruit of these trees they were also much delighted, and the leaves they ate to prevent surfeits and other diseases that are incident to those that heat their blood by travels.

On either side of the river was also a meadow, curiously beautified with lilies, and it was green all the year long. In this meadow they lay down and slept; for here they might lie down safely. When they awoke, they gathered again of the fruit of the trees, and drank again of the water of the river, and then lay down again to sleep. Thus they did several days and nights and when they were disposed to go on, for they were not, as yet, at their journey's end, they ate and drank, and departed.

Now, I beheld in my dream, that they had not journeyed far, but the river and the way for a time parted; at which they were not a little sorry; yet they durst not go out of the way. Now the way from the river was rough, and their feet tender, by reason of their travels. Still as they went on, they wished for a better way. Now, a little before them, there was on the left hand of the road a meadow, and a stile to go over into it; and that meadow is called By-path Meadow. Then said Christian, this meadow lieth along by our wayside, let us go over into it. Then he went to the stile to see, and behold, a path lay along by the way, on the other side of the fence. It is according to my wish, said Christian. Here is the easiest going; come, good Hopeful, and let us go over.

HOPEFUL. But how if this path should lead us out of the way?

CHRISTIAN. That is not likely. Look, doth it not go along by the wayside? So, Hopeful, being persuaded, went after him over the stile. When they were gone over, and were got into the path, they found it very easy for their feet; and they espied a man walking as they did, and his name was Vain-confidence; so they called after him, and asked him whither that way led.

He said, To the Celestial Gate. Look, said Christian, did not I tell you so? By this you may see we are right. So they followed, and he went before them. But, behold, the night came on, and it grew very dark; so that they that were behind lost the sight of him that went before.

He, therefore, that went before (Vain-confidence) not seeing the way before him, fell into a deep pit, which was on purpose there made by the Prince of those grounds, to cath vain-glorious fools withal, and was dashed in pieces with his fall.

Now Christian and his fellow heard him fall. So they called to know the matter, but there was none to answer, only they heard a groaning. Then said Hopeful, Where are we now? Then was his fellow silent, as mistrusting that he had led him out of the way; and now it began to rain, and thunder, and lighten in a very dreadful manner; and the water rose amain.

Then Hopeful groaned, Oh, that I had kept on my way!

CHRISTIAN. Who could have thought that this path should have led us out of the way?

HOPEFUL. I was afraid on it at the very first, and therefore gave you that gentle caution. I would have spoken plainer, but that you are older than I.

CHRISTIAN. Good brother, be not offended; I am sorry I have brought thee out of the way, and that I have put thee into such imminent danger; pray, my brother, forgive me; I did not do it of an evil intent.

HOPEFUL. Be comforted, my brother, for I forgive thee, and I believe, too, that this shall be for our good.

CHRISTIAN. I am glad I have with me a merciful

brother; but we must not stand thus: let us try to go back again.

HOPEFUL. But, good brother, let me go before.

CHRISTIAN. No, if you please, let me go first, that if there be any danger, I may be first therein, because by my means we are both gone out of the way.

HOPEFUL. No, you shall not go first; for your mind being troubled may lead you out of the way again. But by this time the waters were greatly risen, by reason of which the way back was very dangerous. Yet they adventured to go back, but it was dark, and the flood was so high, that in their going back they had like to have been drowned nine or ten times.

Neither could they, with all the skill they had, get again to the stile that night. Wherefore, at last, lighting under a little shelter, they sat down there until the day-break; but, being weary, they fell asleep. Not

VAIN-CONFIDENCE.

far from the place where they lay, was Doubting Castle, the owner whereof was Giant Despair; and it was in his grounds they now were sleeping; wherefore he, getting up in the morning early, and walking up and down in his fields, caught Christian and Hopeful asleep in his grounds. Then, with a grim and surly voice, he bid them awake; and asked them whence they were, and what they did in his grounds. They told him they were pilgrims, and that they had lost their way. Then, said the Giant, You have this night trespassed on me, by trampling in, and lying on my grounds, and therefore you must go along with me. They also had but little to say, for they knew themselves in a fault. The Giant therefore, drove them before him, and put them into a very dark dungeon, nasty and stinking to the spirits of these two men. Here, then, they lay from Wednesday morning till Saturday night, without one bit of bread, or drop of drink, or light ; they were, therefore, here in evil case, and were far from friends and acquaintance. Now in this place Christian had double sorrow, because it was through his unadvised counsel that they were brought into this distress.

Now, Giant Despair had a wife, and her name was Diffidence. So when he was gone to bed, he told his wife that he had taken a couple of prisoners and cast them into his dungeon, for trespassing on his grounds, he asked her also what he had best to do further to them. So she asked him what they were, whence they came, and whither they were bound; and he told her. Then she counselled him that when he arose, in the morning he should beat them without any mercy. So, when he arose, he getteth him a grievous crab-tree cudgel, and goes down into the dungeon to them, and there first falls to rating of them as if they were dogs, although they never gave him a word of distaste. Then he falls upon them, and beats them fearfully, in such sort, that they were not able to help themselves, or to turn them upon the floor. This done, he withdraws and leaves them, there to condole their misery and to mourn under their distress. So all that day they spent the time in nothing but sighs and lamentations. The next night, she, talking with her husband about them further, and understanding they were yet alive, did advice him to counsel them to make away with themselves. So when morning was come, he goes to them in a surly manner as before, and perceiving them to be very sore with the stripes that he had given them the day before, he told them, that since they were never likely to come out of that place, their only way would be forthwith to make an end of themselves, either with knife, halter, or poison, for why, said he, should you choose life, seeing it is attended with so much bitterness? But they desired him to let them go. With that he looked ugly upon them, and rushing to them, had doubtless made an end of them himself, but that he fell into a fit. Then did the prisoners consult between themselves, whether it was the best to take his counsel or no; and thus they began to discourse:

CHRISTIAN. Brother, what shall we do? The life that we now live is miserable. For my part I know not whether it is best, to live thus, or to die out of hand. Shall we be ruled by the Giant?

HOPEFUL. Indeed, our present condition is dreadful, and death would be far more welcome to me than thus for ever to abide; but yet, let us consider, the Lord of the country to which we are going hath said, Thou shalt do no murder. Besides, he that kills another can but commit murder upon his body; but for one to kill himself is to kill body and soul at once.

Well, towards evening, the Giant goes down into the

dungeon again, to see if his prisoners had taken his counsel; but when he came there he found them alive; and truly, alive was all; for now, what for want of bread and water, and by reason of the wounds they received when he beat them, they could do little but breathe.

At this they trembled greatly, and I think that Christian fell into a swoon; but, coming a little to himself again, they renewed their discourse about the Giant's counsel; and whether yet they had best to take it or no.

HOPEFUL. My brother, said he, rememberest thou not how valiant thou hast been heretofore? Apollyon could not crush thee, nor could all that thou didst hear, or see, or feel in the Valley of the Shadow of Death. Wherefore let us bear up with patience as well as we can.

Now, night being come again, and the Giant and his wife being in bed, she asked him concerning the prisoners, and if they had taken his counsel. To which he replied, They are sturdy rogues, and choose rather to bear all hardships, than to make away with themselves. Then said she, Take them into the castle yard to-morrow, and show them the bones and skulls of those that thou hast already despatched, and make them believe, ere a week comes to an end, thou also will tear them in pieces, as thou hast done their fellows before them. So when the morning was come, the Giant goes to them again, and takes them into the castle-yard. These, said he, were once pilgrims as you are, and they tress-passed in my grounds, as you have done; and when I thought fit, I tore them in pieces, and so I will do you. Go, get you down to your den again; and with that he beat them all the way thither. They lay, therefore all

day on Saturday in a lamentable case, as before. Now, when night was come, and when Mrs. Diffidence and her husband, the Giant, were got to bed, they began to renew their discourse of their prisoners; and withal the old Giant wondered, that he could neither by blows nor counsel bring them to an end. And with that his wife replied, I fear, said she, that they live in hope that some will come to relieve them, or that they have pick-locks about them, by the means of which they hope to escape. And sayest thou so, my dear? said the Giant; I will, therefore, search them in the morning.

Well, on Saturday, about mid-night, they began to pray, and continued in prayer till almost break of day. Now, a little before it was day, good Christian, as one half amazed, brake out in this passionate speech: What a fool, quoth he, am I, thus to lie in a stinking dun-geon, when I may as well walk at liberty! I have a key in my bosom, called Promise, that will, I am per-suaded, open any lock in Doubting Castle. Then said Hopeful, That is good news, good brother; pluck it out of thy bosom, and try.

Then Christian pulled it out of his bosom and began to try at the dungeon door, whose bolt gave back, and the door flew open with ease, and Christian and Hope-ful both came out. Then he went to the outward door that leads into the castle-yard, and, with his key, opened that door also. After, he went to the iron-gate, for that must be opened too; but that lock went dam-nable hard, yet the key did open it. Then they thrust open the gate to make their escape with speed, but that gate, as it opened, made such a cracking, that it waked Giant Despair, who, hastily rising to pursue his prison-ers, felt his limbs to fail, for his fits took him again, so that he could by no means go after them. Then they went on, and came to the King's highway, and so were safe, because they were out of his jurisdiction.

Now, when they were gone over the stile, they began to contrive with themselves what they should do at that stile, to prevent those that should come after, from falling into the hands of Giant Despair. So they consented to erect there a pillar, and to engrave upon the side thereof this sentence—"Over this stile is the way to Doubting Castle, which is kept by Giant Despair, who despiseth the King of the Celestial Country, and seeks to destroy his holy Pilgrims." Many, therefore, that followed after, read what was written, and escaped the danger.

They went then till they came to the Delectable Mountains, which belong to the Lord of that hill of which we have spoken before; so they went up to behold the gardens and orchards, the vineyards and fountains, where also they drank and washed themselves, and did freely eat of the vineyards. Now there were on the tops of these mountains shepherds feeding their flocks. The Pilgrims, therefore, went to them, and, leaning upon their staves, they asked, Whose Delectable Mountains are these? and whose be the sheep that feed upon them?

SHEPHERDS. These mountains are Immanuel's Land, and they are within sight of his city; and the sheep also are his, and he laid down his life for them.

CHRISTIAN. Is this the way to the Celestial City?

SHEPHERDS. Your are just in your way.

CHRISTIAN. How far is it thither?

SHEPHERDS. Too far for any but those that shall get thither indeed.

CHRISTIAN. Is there, in this place, any relief for pilgrims that are weary and faint in the way?

SHEPHERDS. The Lord of these mountains hath given us a charge not to be "forgetful to entertain strangers," therefore the good of the place is before you.

I saw also in my dream, that when the Shepherds perceived that they were wayfaring men, also put questions to them. When the Shepherds heard their answers, being pleased therewith, they looked very lovingly upon them.

The Shepherds, whose names were Knowledge, Experience, Watchful, and Sincere, then welcomed the pilgrims to the Delectable Mountains, took them by the hand, and had them to their tents, and made them partake of that which was ready.

Then I saw in my dream, that in the morning the Shepherds called up Christian and Hopeful to walk with them upon the mountains and show them some wonders. They first took them to the top of a hill called Error, which was very deep on the furthest side, and bid them look down to the bottom. So Christian and Hopeful looked down, and saw at the bottom several men dashed all to pieces. These you see, said the Shepherds, erred concerning the faith of the resurrection of the body and they have continued to this day unburied, as an example to others to take heed how they clamber too high or too near the brink of this mountain.

Then I saw that they had them to the top of another mountain, and the name of that is Caution, where they perceived, as they thought, several men walking up and down among the tombs that were there; and they saw that the men were blind, because they stumbled sometimes upon the tombs, and could not get out from among them.

Then I saw in my dream, that the Shepherds had them to another place, in a bottom, where was a door in the side of a hill, and they opened the door. Within it was very dark and smoky, and they heard rumbling noise as of fire, and a cry of some tormented, and they smelt the scent of brimstone. The Shepherds told them, This is a byway to hell, a way that hypocrites go in at; namely, such as sell their birthright, with Esau; such as sell their master, with Judas; such as blaspheme the gospel, with Alexander; and that lie and dissemble, with Ananias and Sapphira his wife. Then said the pilgrims one to another, We have need to cry to the Strong for strength.

By this time the pilgrims had a desire to go forward, and the Shepherds a desire they should; so they walked together towards the end of the mountains. Then said the Shepherds one to another, Let us here show to the pilgrims the gates of the Celestial City, if they have skill to look through our perspective glass. They looked and thought they saw something like the gate, and also of the glory of the place.

When they were about to depart, one of the Shepherds gave them a note of the way. Another of them bid them beware of the Flatterer. The third bid them take heed that they sleep not upon the Enchanted Ground. And the fourth bid them God-speed. So I awoke from my dream.

And I slept, and dreamed again, and saw the same two pilgrims going down the mountains along the highway towards the city. Now, a little below these mountains, on the left hand, lieth the country of Conceit; from which country there comes into the way in which the pilgrims walked, a little crooked lane. Here, therefore, they met with a very brisk lad, that came out of that country; and his name was Ignorance. So Christian asked him from what parts he came. and whither he was going.

IGNORANCE. Sir, I was born in the country that lieth off there a little on the left hand, and I am going to the Celestial City.

CHRISTIAN. But how do you think to get in at the gate? for you may find some difficulty there.

IGNORANCE. I know my Lord's will, and I have been a good liver; I pay every man his own; I pray, fast, pay tithes, and give alms, and have left my country for whither I am going.

CHRISTIAN. But thou camest not in at the wicket-gate that is at the head of this way; thou camest in hither through that same crooked lane, and therefore, I fear, however thou mayest think of thyself, when the reckoning day shall come, thou wilt have laid to thy charge that thou art a thief and a robber, instead of getting admittance into the city.

IGNORANCE. Gentlemen, ye be utter strangers to me, I know you not; be content to follow the religion of your country, and I will follow the religion of mine. I hope all will be well. And as for the gate that you talk of, all the world knows that that is a great way off of our country. I cannot think that any man in all our parts, doth so much as know the way to it, nor need they matter whether they do or no, since we have, as you see, a fine, pleasant green lane, that comes down from our country, into the way.

When Christian saw that the man was "wise in his own conceit," he said to Hopeful, whisperingly, "There is more hope of a fool than of him." Let us pass him by, if you will, and talk to him anon, even as he is able to bear it.

So they both went on, and Ignorance he came after. Now when they had passed him a little way, they entered into a very dark lane, where they met a man whom seven devils had bound with seven strong cords, and were carrying of him back to the door that they saw on the side of the hill. As the devils led away the man, Christian looked to see if he knew him; and he thought it might be one Turn-away, that dwelt in the town of Apostasy. But being once past, Hopeful looked after him, and espied on his back a paper with this inscription, "Wanton professor and damnable apostate."

IGNORANCE.

Now I call to remembrance, said Christian, in this same place a good man named Little Faith who, while on a pilgrimage, as we are now, chanced to sit down and slept. Now there came down the lane, from Broadway Gate, three sturdy rogues, and their names were Faint-heart, Mistrust, and Guilt. The good man was just awake from his sleep, and was getting up to go on his journey. So the three rogues with threatening language bid him stand. Then said Faint-heart, Deliver thy **purse.** But he making no haste to do it, Mistrust ran up to him, and thrusting his hand into his pocket, pulled out thence a bag of silver. Then he cried out, Thieves! Thieves! With that Guilt, with a great club that was in his hand, struck Little-faith on the head, and with that blow felled him flat to the ground, where he lay bleeding as one that would bleed to death. But, at last, they hearing that some were upon the road, and fearing lest it should be one Great-grace, that dwells in the city of Good-confidence, they betook themselves to their heels, and left this good man to shift for himself.

Now, after a while, they perceived afar off, one coming softly, and alone, all along the highway to meet them. Yonder, said Christian, is a man with his back towards Zion, and he is coming to meet us. So he drew nearer and nearer, and at last came up unto them. His name was Atheist, and he asked them whither they were going.

CHRISTIAN. We are going to Mount Zion.

Then Atheist fell into a very great laughter.

CHRISTIAN. What is the meaning of your laughter ?

ATHEIST. I laugh to see what ignorant persons you are, to take upon you so tedious a journey, and you are like to have nothing but your travel for your pains.

CHRISTIAN. Why, man, do you think we shall not be received ?

ATHEIST. Received! There is no such place as you dream of in all this world.

CHRISTIAN. But there is in the world to come.

ATHEIST. When I was at home in mine own country, I heard as you now affirm, and from that hearing went

THEN ATHEIST FELL INTO A VERY GREAT LAUGHTER.

out to see, and have been seeking this city this twenty years; but find no more of it than I did the first day I set out.

CHRISTIAN. We have both heard and believe that there is such a place to be found.

ATHEIST. Had not I, when at home, believed, I had not come thus far to seek; but finding none, I am going back again, and will seek to refresh myself with the things that I then cast away, for hope of that which, I now see is not.

CHRISTIAN then said to Hopeful, Is it true which this man hath said?

HOPEFUL. Take heed, he is one of the flatterers; remember what it hath cost us already for hearkening to such fellows. What! no Mount Zion? Did we not see, from the Delectable Mountains, the gate of the city? Also, are we not now to walk by faith? Let us go on, said Hopeful, lest the man with the whip overtake us again.

CHRISTIAN. My brother, I did not put the question to thee for that I doubted of the truth of our belief myself, but to prove thee, and to fetch from thee a fruit of the honesty of thy heart. As for this man, I know that he is blinded by the god of this world. Let thee and I go on, knowing that we have belief of the truth, "and no lie is of the truth."

HOPEFUL. Now do I rejoice in hope of the glory of God. So they turned away from the man; and he, laughing at them, went his way.

I saw then in my dream, that they went until they came into a certain country whose air naturally tended to make one drowsy, if he came a stranger into it. And here Hopeful began to be very dull and heavy of sleep; wherefore he said unto Christian, I do now begin to grow

The Pilgrim's Progress—4.

"'THREE ROGUES BID HIM STAND.'"

See page 125.

so drowsy, that I can scarcely hold up mine eyes; let us lie down here and take one nap.

CHRISTIAN. By no means, lest sleeping, we never awake more.

HOPEFUL. Why, my brother? Sleep is sweet to the laboring man; we may be refreshed if we take a nap

CHRISTIAN. Do you not remember that one of the Shepherds bid us beware of the Enchanted Ground? He meant by that, that we should beware of sleeping.

HOPEFUL. I acknowledge myself in a fault; and had I been here alone, I had by sleeping run the danger of death.

I saw then in my dream that Hopeful looked back and saw Ignorance, whom they had left behind, coming after. Look, said he to Christian, how far yonder youngster loitereth behind, let us tarry for him. So they did.

CHRISTIAN then said to him, Come away, man; why do you stay so behind?

IGNORANCE. I take my pleasure in walking alone, even more a great deal than in company, unless I like it the better.

CHRISTIAN. Come, how do you? How stands it between God and your soul now?

IGNORANCE. I hope well; for I am always full of good motions, that come into my mind, to comfort me as I walk.

CHRISTIAN. What good motions?

IGNORANCE. Why, I think of God and heaven.

CHRISTIAN. So do the devils and damned souls.

IGNORANCE. But I think of them and desire them.

CHRISTIAN. So do many that are never like to come there.

IGNORANCE.   But I think of them, and leave all for them.

CHRISTIAN.   That I doubt; for leaving all is a hard matter: yea, a harder matter than many are aware of. But why, or by what, art thou persuaded that thou hast left all for God and heaven?

IGNORANCE.   My heart tells me so.

CHRISTIAN.   The wise man says, "He that trusts his own heart is a fool."

IGNORANCE.   This is spoken of an evil heart, but mine is a good one.

CHRISTIAN.   But how dost thou prove that?

IGNORANCE.   It comforts me in hopes of heaven.

CHRISTIAN.   What dost thou believe?

IGNORANCE.   I believe that Christ died for sinners; and that I shall be justified before God from the curse, through his gracious acceptance of my obedience to his law.

CHRISTIAN.   Let me give an answer to this confession of thy faith.

1.   Thou believest with a fantastical faith; for this faith is nowhere described in the Word.   2. Thou believest with a false faith; because it taketh justification from the personal righteousness of Christ, and applies it to thy own.   3. This faith maketh not Christ a justifier of thy person, but of thy actions; and of thy person for thy actions' sake, which is false.   4. Therefore, this faith is deceitful, even such as will leave thee under wrath, in the day of God Almighty.

IGNORANCE.   What! would you have us trust to what Christ, in his own person, has done without us? This conceit would loosen the reins of our lust, and tolerate us to live as we list; for what matter how we live, if we may be justified by Christ's personal righteousness from all, when we believe it?

CHRISTIAN.   Ignorance is thy name, and as thy name is, so art thou; even this thy answer demonstrateth

I AM ALWAYS FULL OF GOOD MOTIONS.

what I say. Ignorant thou art of what justifying righteousness is, and as ignorant how to secure thy soul, through the faith of it, from the heavy wrath of God.

HOPEFUL.   Ask him if ever he had Christ revealed to him from heaven.

IGNORANCE.   What! you are a man for revelations! I believe that what both you say, is but the fruit of distracted brains.

HOPEFUL.   Why, man! Christ is so hid in God from the natural apprehensions of the flesh, that he cannot by any man be savingly known, unless God the Father reveals him to them.

IGNORANCE.   That is your faith, but not mine; yet mine, I doubt not, is as good as yours, though I have not in my head so many whimsies as you.

CHRISTIAN.   You ought not so slightly to speak of this matter; for this I will boldly affirm, that no man can know Jesus Christ but by the revelation of the Father, of which Faith, I perceive, poor Ignorance, thou art ignorant of. Be awakened, then; see thine own wretchedness, and fly to the Lord Jesus; and by his righteousness, which is the righteousness of God, for he himself is God, thou shalt be delivered from condemnation.

IGNORANCE.   You go so fast, I cannot keep pace with you. Do you go on before; I must stay a while behind.

CHRISTIAN.   Well, good Hopeful, I perceive that you and I must walk by ourselves again.

So I saw in my dream that they went on apace before, and Ignorance he came hobbling after.

CHRISTIAN then said, It pities me much for this poor man; it will certainly go ill with him at last.

HOPEFUL.   Alas! there are abundance in our town in his condition; whole families, yea, whole streets. and that of pilgrims, too; and if there be so many in our parts, how many, think you, must there be in the place where he was born? Are we now almost got past the Enchanted Ground?

CHRISTIAN. We have not now above two miles further to go thereon. We will now leave, at this time our neighbor Ignorance and fall upon another profitable question.

HOPEFUL. With all my heart, you shall begin.

CHRISTIAN. About ten years ago, one Temporary who was a forward man in religion, dwelt in Graceless, a town about ten miles off Honesty, and his house was next door to one Turnback. He told me once that he was resolved to go on pilgrimage; but all of a sudden he grew acquainted with one Save-self, and then he became a stranger to me.

HOPEFUL. Now, since we are talking about him, let us inquire into the reason of the sudden backsliding of him and such others. There are in my judgment four reasons for it: 1. Though the consciences of such men are awakened, yet their minds are not changed; therefore when the power of guilt wears away, that which provoked them to be religious ceaseth, wherefore, they naturally turn to their own course again. 2. They have slavish fears that do overmaster them, though they seem to be hot for heaven, so long as the flames of hell are about their ears, yet when that terror is a little over, they betake themselves to second thoughts; and fall in with the world again. 3. The shame that attends religion lies also as a block in their way; they are proud and haughty, and religion in their eyes is low and contemptible. 4. Guilt, and to meditate terror, are grievous to them. But because they shun the thoughts of guilt and terror, when once they are rid of their awakening about the terrors and wrath of God, they harden their hearts gladly, and choose such ways as will harden them more and more.

CHRISTIAN. You are pretty near the business, for the bottom of all is for want of a change in their mind and will.

HOPEFUL. Now I have showed you the reasons of their going back, do you show me the manner thereof.

CHRISTIAN. So I will willingly. 1. They draw off their thoughts, all that they may, from the remembrance of God, death, and judgment to come. 2. Then they cast off by degrees private duties, as closet prayer, curbing their lusts, watching, sorrow for sin, and the like. 3. Then they shun the company of lively and warm Christians. 4. After that they grow cold to public duty, as hearing, reading, godly conference, and the like. 5. Then they begin to pick holes, as we say, in the coats of some of the godly; and that devilishly, that they may have a seeming color to throw religion behind their backs. 6. Then they begin to adhere to, and associate themselves with, carnal, loose, and wanton men. 7. Then they give way to carnal and wanton discourses in secret. 8. After this they begin to play with little sins openly. 9. And then, being hardened, they show themselves as they are. Thus, being launched again into the gulf of misery, unless a miracle of grace prevent it, they everlastingly perish.

Now I saw in my dream, that by this time the pilgrims were got over the Enchanted Ground and entering into the country of Beulah, whose air was very sweet and pleasant; the way lying directly through it, they solaced themselves there for a season. Here they heard continually the singing of birds, and saw every day the flowers appear in the earth, and heard the voice of the turtle in the land. In this country the sun shineth night and day; wherefore this was beyond the Valley of the Shadow of Death, and also out of the reach of Giant Despair, neither could they from this place so much as see Doubting Castle. Here they were within sight of the city they were going to, also here met them some of the inhabitants thereof, for in this land the Shining Ones commonly walked, because it was upon the borders of heaven. Here they had no want of corn and wine; for in this place they met with abundance of what they had sought for in all their pilgrimage. Here all the inhabitants of the country called them, "The holy people, The Redeemed of the Lord, Sought out."

Now, as they walked in this land, they had more rejoicing than in parts more remote from the kingdom to which they were bound; and, drawing near to the city, they had yet a more perfect view thereof. It was builded of pearls and precious stones, also the street thereof was paved with gold; so that by reason of the natural glory of the city, and the reflection of the sun-beams upon it, Christian with desire fell sick; Hopeful also had a fit or two of the same disease. But, being soon a little strengthened, and better able to bear their sickness, they walked on, and came yet nearer and nearer, where were orchards, vineyards, and gardens, and their gates opened into the highway. Now, as they came up to these places, behold the gardener stood in the way, to whom the Pilgrims said, Whose goodly vineyards and gardens are these? He answered, They are the king's, and are planted here for his own delight, and also for the solace of pilgrims. So the gardener had them in the vineyards, and bid them refresh themselves with the dainties. He also showed them there the King's walks, and the arbors where he delighted to be; and here they tarried and slept.

Now I beheld in my dream, that they talked more in their sleep at this time than ever they did in all their journey; and being in a muse thereabout, the gardener said to me, Wherefore musest thou at the matter? It is the nature of the fruit of the grapes of these vineyards to go down so sweetly as to cause the lips of them that are asleep to speak.

So I saw that when they awoke, they addressed themselves to go up to the city; but, as I said, the reflection of the sun upon the city—for "the city was pure gold"—was so extremely glorious, that they could not, as yet, with open face behold it, but through an instrument made for that purpose. So I saw, that as they went on, there met them two men, in raiment that shone like gold; also their faces shone as the light.

These men asked the Pilgrims whence they came; and they told them. They also asked them where they had lodged, what difficulties and dangers, what comforts and pleasures, they had met with in the way; and they told them. Then said the men that met them, You have but two difficulties more to meet with, and then you are in the city.

Christian then, and his companion, asked the men to go along with them; so they told them they would. But, said they, you must obtain it by your own faith. So they went on together, until they came in sight of the gate.

Now, I further saw, that betwixt them and the gate was a river, but there was no bridge to go over; the river was very deep. At the sight, therefore, of this river, the pilgrims were much stunned; but the men that went with them said, You must go through, or you cannot come at the gate.

The pilgrims then began to inquire if there was no other way to the gate; to which they answered, Yes; but there hath not any, save two, to wit, Enoch and Elijah, been permitted to tread that path, since the foundation of the world, nor shall, until the last trumpet shall sound. The pilgrims then, especially Christian, began to despond in their minds, and looked this way and that, but no way could be found by them, by which they might escape the river. Then they asked the men if the waters were all of a depth. They said, No; yet they could not help them in that case; for, said they, you shall find it deeper or shallower as you believe in the King of the place.

Then they addressed themselves to the water; and entering, Christian began to sink, and crying out to his good friend Hopeful, he said, I sink in deep waters; the billows go over my head, all his waves go over me!

Then said the other, Be of good cheer, my brother, I feel the bottom, and it is good. Then said Christian, Ah! my friend, "the sorrows of death have compassed me about;" I shall not see the land that flows with milk and honey; and with that a great darkness and horror fell upon Christian, so that he could not see before him. Also he in great measure lost his senses, so that he could neither remember, nor orderly talk of any of those sweet refreshments that he had met with in the way of his pilgrimage. But all the words that he spake still tended to discover that he had horror of mind, and heart fears that he should die in that river, and never obtain entrance in at the gate. Here also, he was much in the troublesome thoughts of the sins that he had committed, both since and before he began to be a pilgrim. It was also observed that he was troubled with apparitions of hobgoblins and evil spirits, for ever and anon he would intimate so much by words. Hopeful, therefore, here had much ado to keep his brother's head above water; yea, sometimes he would be quite gone down, and then, he would rise up again half dead. Hopeful would endeavor to comfort him, saying, Brother, I see the gate, and men standing by to receive us; but Christian would answer, It is you, it is you they wait for; you have been Hopeful ever since I knew you. And so have you, said he to Christian. Ah, brother! said Christian, surely if I was right he would now rise to help me; but for my sins he hath brought me into the snare, and hath left me. Then said Hopeful, My brother, you have quite forgot the text where it is said of the wicked, "There are no bands in their death, but their strength is firm. They are not in trouble as other men, neither are they plagued like other men." These troubles and distresses that you go through in these waters are no sign that God hath forsaken you; but are sent to try you, whether you will call to mind that which heretofore you have received of his goodness, and live upon him in your distresses.

Then I saw in my dream that Christian was in a muse a while. To whom also Hopeful added this word, Be of good cheer. Jesus Christ maketh thee whole; and with that Christian brake out with a loud voice, Oh! I see him again, and he tells me, "When thou passest through the waters, I will be with thee; and through the rivers, they shall not overflow thee." Then they both took courage, and the enemy was after that as still as a stone, until they were gone over. Christian therefore presently found ground to stand upon, and so it fol-

lowed that the rest of the river was but shallow. Thus they got over. Now, upon the bank of the river, on the other side, they saw the two shining men again, who there waited for them; wherefore, being come out of the river, they saluted them, saying, We are ministering spirits, sent forth to minister for those that shall be heirs of salvation. Thus they went along towards the gate.

Now you must note that the city stood upon a mighty hill, but the pilgrims went up that hill with ease, because they had these two men to lead them up by the arms; also, they had left their mortal garments behind them in the river, for though they went in with them, they came out without them. They, therefore, went up here with much agility and speed, though the foundation upon which the city was framed was higher than the clouds. They went up through the regions of the air, sweetly talking as they went, being comforted, because they safely got over the river, and had such glorious companions to attend them.

The talk they had with the Shining Ones was about the glory of the place; who told them that the beauty and glory of it was inexpressible. There, said they, is "Mount Zion, the heavenly Jerusalem, the innumerable company of angels, and the spirits of just men made perfect." You are going now, said they, to the Paradise of God, wherein you shall see the tree of life, and eat of the never-fading fruits thereof; and when you come there, you shall have white robes given you, and your walk and talk shall be every day with the King, even all the days of eternity. There you shall not see again such things as you saw when you were in the lower region upon the earth, to wit, sorrow, sickness, affliction, and death, "for the former things are passed away." You are now going to Abraham, to Isaac, and Jacob, and to the prophets—men that God hath taken away from the evil to come, and that are now resting upon their beds, each one walking in his righteousness. The man then asked, What must we do in the holy place? To whom it was answered, You must there receive the comforts of all your toil, and have joy for all your sorrow; you must reap what you have sown, even the fruit of all your prayers, and tears, and sufferings for the King by the way. In that place you must wear crowns of gold, and enjoy the perpetual sight of the Holy One, for "there you shall see him as he is." There also you shall serve him continually with praise, with shouting, and thanksgiving, whom you desired to serve in the world, though with

THUS THEY GOT OVER.

much difficulty, because of the infirmity of your flesh. There your eyes shall be delighted with seeing, and your ears with hearing the pleasant voice of the Mighty One. There you shall enjoy your friends again, that are gone thither before you; and there you shall with joy receive every one that follows into the holy place after you. There also shall you be clothed with glory and majesty, and put into an equipage fit to ride out with the King of Glory. When he shall come with sound of trumpet in the clouds, as upon the wings of the wind, you shall come with him; and when he shall sit upon the throne of judgment, you shall sit by him; yea, and when he shall pass sentence upon all the workers of iniquity, let them be angels or men, you also shall have a voice in that judgment, because they were his and your enemies. Also, when he shall again return to the city, you shall go too, with sound of trumpet, and be ever with him.

Now, while they were thus drawing towards the gate, behold a company of the heavenly host came out to meet them; to whom it was said, by the other two Shining Ones, These are the men that have loved our Lord when they were in the world, and that have left all for his holy name; and he hath sent us to fetch them, and we have brought them thus far on their desired journey, that they may go in and look their Redeemer in the face with joy. Then the heavenly host gave a great shout, saying, "Blessed are they which are called unto the marriage supper of the Lamb." There came out also at this time to meet them several of the King's trumpeters, clothed in white and shining raiment, who, with melodious noises, and loud, made even the heavens to echo with their sound. These trumpeters saluted Christian and his fellow with ten thousand welcomes, and this they did with shouting, and sound of trumpet.

This done, they compassed them round on every side;

some went before, some behind, and some on the right hand, some on the left (as it were to guard them through the upper regions), continually sounding as they went, in notes on high: so that it was to them that could behold it, as if heaven itself was come down to meet them. Thus, they walked on together; and as they walked, ever and anon these trumpeters, with joyful sound, would, by mixing their music with looks and gestures, still signify to Christian and his brother how welcome they were into their company, and with what gladness they came to meet them; and now were these two men, as it were, in heaven before they came at it, being swallowed up with the sights of angels, and with hearing of their melodious notes. Here also they had the city itself in view, and they

ONE OF THE KING'S TRUMPETERS.

thought they heard all the bells therein to ring, to welcome them thereto. But above all, the warm and joyful thoughts that they had about their own dwelling there, with such company, and that forever and ever. Oh, by what tongue or pen can their glorious joy be expressed! And thus they came up to the gate, over which was written in letters of gold, "Blessed are they that do his commandments, that they may have right to the tree of life, and may enter in through the gates into the city."

Then I saw in my dream that the Shining Men bid them call at the gate; the which, when they did, some looked from above over the gate, to wit, Enoch, Moses, and Elijah, etc., to whom it was said, These pilgrims are come from the City of Destruction, for the love that they bear to the King of this place; and then the pilgrims gave in unto them each man his certificate, which they had received in the beginning; those, therefore, were carried in to the King, who, when he had read them, said, where are the men? To whom it was answered, They are standing without the gate. The King then commanded to open the gate, "That the righteous nation," said he, "which keepeth the truth may enter in."

Now I saw in my dream that these two men went in at the gate; and lo, as they entered, they were transfigured, and they had raiment put on that shone like gold. There were also that met them with harps and crowns, and gave them to them—the harps to praise withal, and the crowns in token of honor. Then I heard in my dream that all the bells in the city rang again for joy, and that it was said unto them, "ENTER YE INTO THE JOY OF YOUR LORD." I also heard the men themselves, that they sang with a loud voice, saying, "BLESSING, AND HONOR, AND GLORY, AND POWER, BE UNTO HIM THAT

SITTETH UPON THE THRONE, AND UNTO THE LAMB, FOR
EVER AND EVER."

Now, just as the gates were opened to let in the men,
I looked in after them, and, behold, the City shone like
the sun; the streets also were paved with gold, and in
them walked many men, with crowns on their heads,
palms in their hands, and golden harps to sing praises
withal.

There were also of them that had wings, and they
answered one another without intermission, saying,
"Holy, holy, holy is the Lord." And after that they
shut up the gates; which, when I had seen, I wished
myself among them.

Now while I was gazing upon all these things, I
turned my head to look back, and saw Ignorance come
up to the river side; but he soon got over, and that without half the difficulty which the other two men met with.
For it happened that there was then in that place one
Vain-hope, a ferryman, that with his boat helped him
over; so he, as the other I saw, did ascend the hill, to
come up to the gate, only he came alone; neither did
any man meet him with the least encouragement. When
he was come up to the gate, he looked up to the writing that was above, and then began to knock, supposing that entrance should have been quickly administered
to him; but he was asked by the men that looked over
the top of the gate, Whence came you? and what would
you have? He answered, I have eat and drank in the
presence of the King, and he has taught in our streets.
Then they asked him for his certificate, that they might
go in and show it to the King; so he fumbled in his
bosom for one, and found none. Then they said, Have
you none? But the man answered never a word. So
they told the King, but he would not come down to see

him, but commanded the two Shining Ones that conducted Christian and Hopeful to the City, to go out and take Ignorance, and bind him hand and foot, and have him away. Then they took him up, and carried him, through the air, to the door that I saw in the side of the hill, and put him in there. Then I saw that there was a way to hell, even from the gates of heaven, as well as from the City of Destruction.

So I awoke, and behold it was a dream.

CONCLUSION.

NOW, reader, I have told my dream to thee
    See if thou canst interpret it to me,
Or to thyself or neighbor; but take heed
Of misinterpreting; for that, instead
Of doing good, will but thyself abuse:
By misinterpreting, evil ensues.

    Take heed also that thou be not extreme
In playing with the outside of my dream;
Nor let my figure or similitude
Put thee into a laughter or a feud.
Leave this for boys and fools; but as for thee,
Do thou the substance of my matter see.

    Put by the curtains, look within my veil;
Turn up my metaphors, and do not fail,
There, if thou seekest them, such things to find
As will be helpful to an honest mind.

    What of my dross thou findest there, be bold
To throw away; but yet preserve the gold.
What if my gold be wrappèd up in ore?—
None throws away the apple for the core.
But if thou shalt cast all away as vain,
I know not but 'twill make me dream again

THE STORY OF THE FROZEN SEAS.   70 illustrations.

WOOD'S NATURAL HISTORY.   80 illustrations.

BLACK BEAUTY.   By Anna Sewell.   50 illustrations.

ARABIAN NIGHTS' ENTERTAINMENTS.   130 illustrations.

ANDERSEN'S FAIRY TALES.   75 illustrations.

GRIMM'S FAIRY TALES.   50 illustrations.

FLOWER FABLES.   By Louisa M. Alcott.   50 illustrations.

AUNT MARTHA'S CORNER CUPBOARD.   By Mary and Elizabeth Kirby.   54 illustrations.

WATER BABIES.   By Charles Kingsley.   84 illustrations.

UNCLE TOM'S CABIN.   90 illustrations.

TALES FROM SHAKESPEARE.   By Charles and Mary Lamb. 65 illustrations.

ADVENTURES IN TOYLAND.   70 illustrations.

ADVENTURES OF A BROWNIE.   18 illustrations.

MIXED PICKLES.   31 illustrations.

LITTLE LAME PRINCE.   By Miss Mulock.   24 illustrations.

THE SLEEPY KING.   77 illustrations.

RIP VAN WINKLE.   By Washington Irving.   46 illustrations.

A CHILD'S GARDEN OF VERSES.   By Robert Louis Stevenson.   100 illustrations.

ANIMAL STORIES FOR LITTLE PEOPLE.   50 illustrations.

CHRISTOPHER COLUMBUS AND THE DISCOVERY OF
AMERICA. 70 illustrations.

HERNANDO CORTEZ, THE CONQUEROR OF MEXICO. By
Jacob Abbott. 30 illustrations.

QUEEN ELIZABETH, OF ENGLAND. By Jacob Abbott. 49
illustrations.

MARY, QUEEN OF SCOTS. By Jacob Abbott. 45 illustrations.

GRANDFATHER'S CHAIR. By Nathaniel Hawthorne. 68 illustrations.

KING CHARLES THE FIRST, OF ENGLAND. By Jacob Abbott. 41 illustrations.

KING CHARLES THE SECOND, OF ENGLAND. By Jacob
Abbott. 28 illustrations.

MADAME ROLAND, A HEROINE OF THE FRENCH REVO-
LUTION. By Jacob Abbott. 42 illustrations.

MARIE ANTOINETTE, QUEEN OF FRANCE. By John S. C.
Abbott. 41 illustrations.

JOSEPHINE, EMPRESS OF FRANCE. By Jacob Abbott. 40
illustrations.

BATTLES OF THE WAR FOR INDEPENDENCE. By Prescott Holmes. 70 illustrations.

MILITARY HEROES OF THE UNITED STATES. 60 illustrations.

HEROES OF THE UNITED STATES NAVY. 60 illustrations.

LIVES OF THE PRESIDENTS OF THE UNITED STATES.
With portraits and illustrations.

BATTLES OF THE WAR FOR THE UNION. By Prescott
Holmes. 80 illustrations.

YOUNG PEOPLE'S HISTORY OF THE WAR WITH SPAIN.
50 illustrations.

Altemus' Illustrated
Mother Goose Series

A series of entirely new editions of the most popular books for young people. Handsomely printed from large, clear type, on choice paper; each volume containing about one hundred illustrations. Half vellum, with illuminated sides (6⅞ x 8¾ inches). Price, 50 cents each.

ALADDIN; OR, THE WONDERFUL LAMP.—OUR ANIMAL FRIENDS.—BEAUTY AND THE BEAST.—BIRD STORIES FOR LITTLE PEOPLE.—CINDERELLA; OR, THE LITTLE GLASS SLIPPER.—THE HOUSE THAT JACK BUILT.—JACK AND THE BEAN-STALK.—JACK THE GIANT-KILLER.—LITTLE RED RIDING HOOD.—PUSS IN BOOTS.—THE SLEEPING BEAUTY.—WHO KILLED COCK ROBIN?

Altemus' Illustrated
Little Men and Women Series

A new series for young people, by the best known English and American authors. Profusely illustrated, and with handsome and appropriate bindings. Cloth, 12mo. Price, 50 cts. each.

BLACK BEAUTY. By Anna Sewell.

HIAWATHA. By Henry W. Longfellow.

ALICE IN WONDERLAND AND THROUGH THE LOOKING GLASS. By

Lewis Carroll.

PAUL AND VIRGINIA. By Sainte Pierre.

Altemus' Illustrated Little Men and Women Series, Continued

GALOPOFF, THE TALKING PONY. By Tudor Jenks.

GYPSY, THE TALKING DOG. By Tudor Jenks.

CAPS AND CAPERS. By Gabrielle E. Jackson.

DOUGHNUTS AND DIPLOMAS. By Gabrielle E. Jackson.

FOR PREY AND SPOILS. By Frederick A. Ober.

TOMMY FOSTER'S ADVENTURES. By Frederick A. Ober.

TALES FROM SHAKESPEARE. By Charles and Mary Lamb.

A LITTLE ROUGH RIDER. By Tudor Jenks.

ANOTHER YEAR WITH DENISE AND NED TOODLES. By Gabrielle E. Jackson.

POOR BOYS' CHANCES. By John Habberton.

SEA KINGS AND NAVAL HEROES. By Hartwell James.

POLLY PERKINS'S ADVENTURES. By E. Louise Liddell.

FOLLY IN FAIRYLAND. By Carolyn Wells.

FOLLY IN THE FOREST. By Carolyn Wells.

THE BOY GEOLOGIST. By Prof. E. J. Houston.

HELEN'S BABIES. By John Habberton.

Altemus' Illustrated
Wee Books for Wee Folks

Filled with charming stories, beautifully illustrated with pictures in colors and black and white. Daintily, yet durably bound. Price, 50 cents each.

NURSERY TALES.—NURSERY RHYMES.—THE STORY OF PETER RABBIT.—THE FOOLISH FOX.—THREE LITTLE PIGS.—THE ROBBER KITTEN.

Children's Gift Series

A new series of the most famous children's classics, in new and attractive bindings with full page illustrations in color and black and white. Cloth, 4to, 75 cents each.

ALICE'S ADVENTURES IN WONDERLAND.—THROUGH THE LOOKING GLASS AND WHAT ALICE FOUND THERE.—A CHILD'S GARDEN OF VERSES.—MOTHER GOOSE'S RHYMES, JINGLES AND FAIRY TALES.—SWISS FAMILY ROBINSON.—THE ADVENTURES OF ROBINSON CRUSOE.—GRIMM'S FAIRY TALES.—ANDERSEN'S FAIRY TALES.—BIBLE PICTURES AND STORIES.—ANIMAL STORIES FOR LITTLE PEOPLE.

One-Syllable Series
For Young Readers

Embracing popular works arranged for the young folks in words of one syllable. With numerous illustrations by the best artists. Handsomely bound, with illuminated covers. Price, 50 cents each.

ÆSOP'S FABLES.—A CHILD'S LIFE OF CHRIST.—THE ADVENTURES OF ROBINSON CRUSOE.—BUNYAN'S PILGRIM'S PROGRESS.—SWISS FAMILY ROBINSON.—GULLIVER'S TRAVELS.—A CHILD'S STORY OF THE OLD TESTAMENT.—A CHILD'S STORY OF THE NEW TESTAMENT.—BIBLE STORIES FOR LITTLE CHILDREN.—THE STORY OF JESUS.

Altemus' Illustrated

Dainty Series of Choice Gift Books

Bound in half-white vellum, illuminated sides, unique designs in gold and colors, with numerous half-tone illustrations. Price, 50 cents each.

THE SILVER BUCKLE. By M. Nataline Crumpton

CHARLES DICKENS' CHILDREN STORIES.

THE CHILDREN'S SHAKESPEARE.

YOUNG ROBIN HOOD. By G. Manville Fenn.

HONOR BRIGHT. By Mary C. Rowsell.

THE VOYAGE OF THE MARY ADAIR. By Frances E. Crompton.

THE KINGFISHER'S EGG. By L. T. Meade.

TATTINE. By Ruth Ogden.

THE DOINGS OF A DEAR LITTLE COUPLE. By Mary D. Brine.

OUR SOLDIER BOY. By G. Manville Fenn.

THE LITTLE SKIPPER. By G. Manville Fenn.

LITTLE GERVAISE AND OTHER STORIES.

THE CHRISTMAS FAIRY. By John Strange Winter.

MOLLY THE DRUMMER BOY. By Harriet T. Comstock.

HOW A "DEAR LITTLE COUPLE" WENT ABROAD. By Mary D. Brine.

THE ROSE-CARNATION. By Frances E. Crompton.

MOTHER'S LITTLE MAN. By Mary D. Brine.

LITTLE SWAN MAIDENS. By Frances E. Crompton.

LITTLE LADY VAL. By Evelyn Everett Green.

A YOUNG HERO. By G. Manville Fenn.

QUEEN OF THE DAY. By L. T. Meade.

THAT LITTLE FRENCH BABY. By John Strange Winter.

THE POWDER MONKEY. By G. Manville Fenn.

THE DOLL THAT TALKED. By Tudor Jenks.

WHAT CHARLIE FOUND TO DO. By Amanda M. Douglas.

Altemus'
Young Folks Puzzle Pictures' Series

A new series for young people, including numerous Puzzle Pictures by the best artists. Full cloth, illuminated cover design. Price, 50 cents each.

MOTHER GOOSE'S PUZZLE PICTURES.
THE TALE OF PETER RABBIT, WITH PUZZLE PICTURES.
ANIMAL TALES, WITH PUZZLE PICTURES.
THE NIGHT BEFORE CHRISTMAS, WITH PUZZLE PICTURES.
DOG TALES, CAT TALES AND OTHER TALES, WITH PUZZLE PICTURFS.

Altemus' Illustrated
Mother Stories Series

An entirely new series, including the best stories that mothers can tell their children. Handsomely printed and profusely illustrated. Ornamental cloth. Price, 50 cents each.

MOTHER STORIES. 89 illustrations.
MOTHER NURSERY RHYMES AND TALES. 135 illustrations.
MOTHER FAIRY TALES. 117 illustrations.
MOTHER NATURE STORIES. 97 illustrations.
MOTHER STORIES FROM THE OLD TESTAMENT. 45 illustrations.
MOTHER STORIES FROM THE NEW TESTAMENT. 45 illustrations.
MOTHER BEDTIME STORIES. 86 illustrations.
MOTHER ANIMAL STORIES. 92 illustrations.
MOTHER BIRD STORIES. 131 illustrations.
MOTHER SANTA CLAUS STORIES. 91 illustrations.

The Motor Boat Club Series

By H. IRVING HANCOCK

The keynote of these books is manliness. The stories are wonderfully entertaining, and they are at the same time sound and wholesome. No boy will willingly lay down an unfinished book in this series.

1 THE MOTOR BOAT CLUB OF THE KENNEBEC; Or, The Secret of Smugglers' Island.

2 THE MOTOR BOAT CLUB AT NANTUCKET; Or, The Mystery of the Dunstan Heir.

3 THE MOTOR BOAT CLUB OFF LONG ISLAND; Or, A Daring Marine Game at Racing Speed.

4 THE MOTOR BOAT CLUB AND THE WIRELESS; Or, The Dot, Dash and Dare Cruise.

5 THE MOTOR BOAT CLUB IN FLORIDA; Or, Laying the Ghost of Alligator Swamp.

6 THE MOTOR BOAT CLUB AT THE GOLDEN GATE; Or, A Thrilling Capture in the Great Fog.

7 THE MOTOR BOAT CLUB ON THE GREAT LAKES; Or, The Flying Dutchman of the Big Fresh Water.

Cloth, Illustrated   Price, per Volume, 50c.

The Range and Grange Hustlers

By FRANK GEE PATCHIN

Have you any idea of the excitements, the glories of life on great ranches in the West? Any bright boy will "devour" the books of this series, once he has made a start with the first volume.

1 THE RANGE AND GRANGE HUSTLERS ON THE RANCH; Or, The Boy Shepherds of the Great Divide.

2 THE RANGE AND GRANGE HUSTLERS' GREATEST ROUND-UP; Or, Pitting Their Wits Against a Packers' Combine.

3 THE RANGE AND GRANGE HUSTLERS ON THE PLAINS; Or, Following the Steam Plows Across the Prairie.

4 THE RANGE AND GRANGE HUSTLERS AT CHICAGO; Or, The Conspiracy of the Wheat Pit.

Cloth, Illustrated   Price, per Volume, 50c.

Submarine Boys Series

By VICTOR G. DURHAM

These splendid books for boys and girls deal with life aboard submarine torpedo boats, and with the adventures of the young crew, and possess, in addition to the author's surpassing knack of story-telling, a great educational value for all young readers.

1 THE SUBMARINE BOYS ON DUTY; Or, Life on a Diving Torpedo Boat.
2 THE SUBMARINE BOYS' TRIAL TRIP; Or, "Making Good" as Young Experts.
3 THE SUBMARINE BOYS AND THE MIDDIES; Or, The Prize Detail at Annapolis.
4 THE SUBMARINE BOYS AND THE SPIES; Or, Dodging the Sharks of the Deep.
5 THE SUBMARINE BOYS' LIGHTNING CRUISE; Or, The Young Kings of the Deep.
6 THE SUBMARINE BOYS FOR THE FLAG; Or, Deeding Their Lives to Uncle Sam.
7 THE SUBMARINE BOYS AND THE SMUGGLERS; Or, Breaking Up the New Jersey Customs Frauds.

Cloth, Illustrated   Price, per Volume, 50c.

The Square Dollar Boys Series

By H. IRVING HANCOCK

The reading boy will be a voter within a few years; these books are bound to make him think, and when he casts his vote he will do it more intelligently for having read these volumes.

1 THE SQUARE DOLLAR BOYS WAKE UP; Or, Fighting the Trolley Franchise Steal.
2 THE SQUARE DOLLAR BOYS SMASH THE RING; Or, In the Lists Against the Crooked Land Deal.

Cloth, Illustrated   Price, per Volume, 50c.

Ben Lightbody Series

By WALTER BENHAM

1 BEN LIGHTBODY, SPECIAL; Or, Seizing His First Chance to Make Good.
2 BEN LIGHTBODY'S BIGGEST PUZZLE; Or, Running the Double Ghost to Earth.

Cloth, Illustrated   Price, per Volume, 50c.

Pony Rider Boys Series

By FRANK GEE PATCHIN

These tales may be aptly described as those of a new Cooper. In every sense they belong to the best class of books for boys and girls.

1. THE PONY RIDER BOYS IN THE ROCKIES; Or, The Secret of the Lost Claim.
2. THE PONY RIDER BOYS IN TEXAS; Or, The Veiled Riddle of the Plains.
3. THE PONY RIDER BOYS IN MONTANA; Or, The Mystery of the Old Custer Trail.
4. THE PONY RIDER BOYS IN THE OZARKS; Or, The Secret of Ruby Mountain.
5. THE PONY RIDER BOYS IN THE ALKALI; Or, Finding a Key to the Desert Maze.
6. THE PONY RIDER BOYS IN NEW MEXICO; Or, The End of the Silver Trail.
7. THE PONY RIDER BOYS IN THE GRAND CANYON; Or, The Mystery of Bright Angel Gulch.

Cloth, Illustrated   Price, per Volume, 50c.

=====

The Boys of Steel Series

By JAMES R. MEARS

The author has made of these volumes a series of romances with scenes laid in the iron and steel world. Each book presents a vivid picture of some phase of this great industry. The information given is exact and truthful; above all, each story is full of adventure and fascination.

1. THE IRON BOYS IN THE MINES; Or, Starting at the Bottom of the Shaft.
2. THE IRON BOYS AS FOREMEN; Or, Heading the Diamond Drill Shift.
3. THE IRON BOYS ON THE ORE BOATS; Or, Roughing It on the Great Lakes.
4. THE IRON BOYS IN THE STEEL MILLS; Or, Beginning Anew in the Cinder Pits.

Cloth, Illustrated   Price, per Volume, 50c.